365
WAYS
TO
CALM
YOUR
CRYING
BABY

Julian Orenstein, M.D.

Adams Media Corporation
Holbrook, Massachusetts

**With love and appreciation for my patient wife Hindy
and our 3 little babies.**

Copyright ©1998 Julian Orenstein. All rights reserved. This book, or parts thereof, may not be reproduced in any form without permission from the publisher;
exceptions are made for brief excerpts used in published reviews.

Published by
Adams Media Corporation
260 Center Street, Holbrook, MA 02343

ISBN: 1-58062-011-6

Printed in Canada.

J I H G F E D C

Library of Congress Cataloging-in-Publication Data
365 ways to calm a crying baby / Julian Orenstein.—1st ed.
ISBN 1-58062-011-6
1. Crying in infants—Popular works. 2. Infants (Newborn)—Care—Popular works.
3. Infants—Care—Popular works. 4. Infants—Health and hygiene—Popular works.
5. Child rearing—Popular works. I. Title.
RJ61.069   1998
649'.122—dc21   98-17607
                              CIP

Many of the designations used by manufacturers and sellers to distinguish their products are claimed as trademarks. Where those designations appear in this book and Adams Media was aware of a trademark claim, the designations have been printed in initial capital letters (e.g. Dacron).

This publication is designed to provide accurate and authoritative information with regard to the subject matter covered. It is sold with the understanding that the publisher is not engaged in rendering legal, accounting, or other professional advice. If legal advice or other expert assistance is required, the services of a competent professional person should be sought.
— From a *Declaration of Principles* jointly adopted by a Committee of the American Bar Association and a Committee of Publishers and Associations

Illustrations by Barry Littmann

*This book is available at quantity discounts for bulk purchases.
For information, call 1-800-872-5627 (in Massachusetts, 781-767-8100).*

Visit our home page at http://www.adamsmedia.com

Contents
0–3 Months: The First Weeks of Infancy

1: Learn her different cries

2: Act now!

3: The rooting reflex

4: The car

5: Vibrating teddies

6: High-contrast mobiles

7: It's a snap

8: Swaddling

9: Warm the wipes

10: Singing

11: Live music

12: The stroller

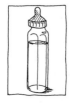   

13: Drinking water **14: Your thumb** **15: Get out the burps, part 1** **16: Swing time**

17: Song: "Over in the Meadow" **18: Rocking chair** **19: I'm just bored** **20: Lambskin rug**

21: Running water **22: Song: "Nobody Likes Me"** **23: Music box** **24: Stationary bicycle ride**

25: Carry her!

26: To poop or not to poop?

27: You can't spoil a baby

28: Song: "Michael Finnegan"

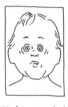

29: Sensory overload, part 1

30: Sensory overload, part 2

31: White noise tapes

32: Feed him!

33: Check the diaper —again?!

34: Sleep

35: Song: "Clap Your Hands"

36: Warm her up!

365 WAYS TO CALM YOUR CRYING BABY

37: Cool him down!

38: Give her a cuddle

39: At-home dad

40: Colic, part 1

41: Colic, part 2

42: Sing her praises

43: The football hold

44: Neck nuzzling

45: Fight the gas

46: "Calming" overload

47: Coo and carry

48: Song: "Alice the Camel"

49: Don't even think about it: Shaking

50: Give in to the colic

51: Off schedule

52: Get out the burps, part 2

53: The miracle reflex

54: The dishwasher

55: Puppets

56: The trick to transferring

57: Change the formula

58: Roll out the great books

59: Leg exercise

60: Bathtime

61: Koala walk

62: Song: "The Eensy Weensy Spider"

63: Song: "Glunk, Glunk, Glunk"

64: Start a ritual

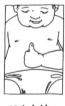

65: Look: I have a thumb!

66: Toys, part 1

67: Toys, part 2

68: Just say no: Tobacco

69: Song: "Hush, Little Baby"

70: Song: "Keemo Kymo"

71: Change your bottle nipple

72: Front carriers

73: SleepTight®

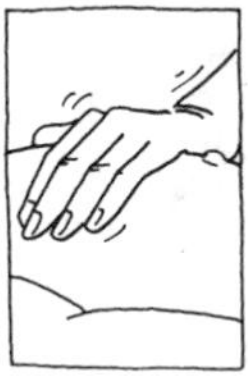

74: Tummy massage

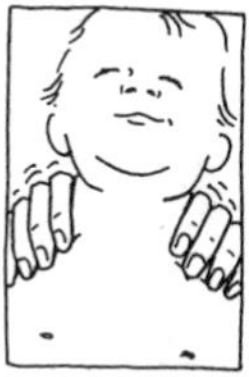

75: Allover massage

76: Song: "Kookaburra"

77: Song: "Lullaby and Good Night"

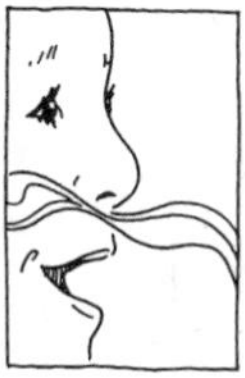

78: Aromatherapy

79: Six states of baby awareness

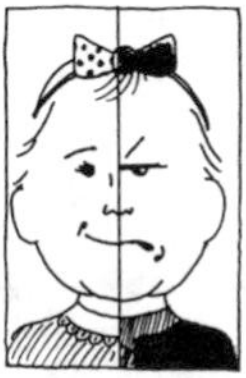

80: The inconsistent baby

81: The jittery baby

82: The high-intensity baby

83: The negative baby

84: The active baby

85: The easy baby

86: Song: "A Welsh Lullaby"

87: Song: "No, No, Yes, Yes"

88: Boxing lessons

89: Make eye contact

90: Take him with you

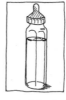

91: Don't force food

92: Formula with iron

93: Song: "There Was an Old Woman Who Swallowed a Fly"

94: Song: "Waltzing Matilda"

95: Bunkmates

96: The early riser

365 WAYS TO CALM YOUR CRYING BABY

97: A new mattress

98: Turn off the noise

99: Chest rub

100: Song: Irish Lullaby ("Too-Ra-Loo-Ra-Loo")

101: Song: "Little Bunny Foo Foo"

102: Nature's Cradle®

103: Rotate diapering

104: Belly raspberries

105: Snuggle game: Leg, foot, toe toe toe

106: Snuggle game: Where is thumbkin?

107: Snuggle game: This little piggy

108: Milk allergy

109: Stuffy nose

110: Don't sweat a runny nose

111: Pacifiers

112: Another great reflex

113: Jiggled, not stirred

114: Just say no: Roughhousing

115: Switch detergents

116: Cold care

117: Try a parenting course

118: Call your mother

119: Teaching others about your infant

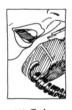

120: The long-distance rescue

365 WAYS TO CALM YOUR CRYING BABY

121: Be prepared!

122: Fever, part 1

123: Discovering an incarcerated hernia

124: Just say no: broccoli

125: Reflux

126: Gastroenteritis

127: Don't even think about it: Herb teas

128: Anal fissures

129: After a DPT shot

130: Don't even think about it: Alcohol

131: Corneal abrasion

132: Hair tourniquet

365 WAYS TO CALM YOUR CRYING BABY

133: Birth injury symptoms

134: Thrush

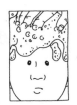

135: Eczema

136: Don't even think about it: Adult medication

137: Keep a record

138: Feeling guilty

139: The hand-off

140: Go public

141: Positive reinforcement

142: Song: "Five Little Monkeys"

3–12 Months: Babyhood

143: Bubbles

144: Car keys

145: Another Stroller Technique

146: Di-di-di-di-di-DEEE

147: Counting blue cars

148: Call the "uh-oh" squad!

149: Subscription cards

150: Cozy, cozy crib

151: Activity: rocker

152: Instant rattle

153: Mega-ball

154: "Hot!"

155: Substitution

156: Diaper rash, part 1

157: Diaper rash, part 2

158: Sitting up

159: Nice, nice, nice, boo!

160: Food allergy

161: Lactose intolerance

162: Fever, part 2

163: Colds

164: Teething, part 1

165: Viral rashes

166: Dehydration

167: Sunburn

168: Chemicals in the eye

169: Stranger anxiety

170: Stranger dislike

171: Babies just wanna play all day

172: Choking, part 1

173: Choking, part 2

174: Song: "The Wheels on the Bus"

175: Mommy's home: decompress!

176: Fears

177: Is baby home?

178: Rolling over

179: Head banging

180: Jumping seat

181: I see me

182: I see me me me me me

183: Naps

184: Peekaboo

185: Music for adults that kids love

186: A Flemish song

187: Funny voices

188: Teething, part 2

189: Finger games

190: Install a car sunshade

191: Make the car seat comfy

192: Toss those tears away

193: Snacks

194: The diaper song

195: Make a tape

196: Grab daddy's glasses

197: More Puppet Games

198: For working moms (and dads, too)

199: Crying at the sight of daddy

200: Knee games

201: Photo gallery

202: Toy rotation

203: Bike trailer

204: Ear care

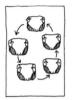

205: The play yard: do's

206: Not *you!*

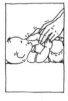

207: Get down!

208: Watch the snacking

209: Taking a fall

210: Read a book

211: Backpack

212: Nap at the right time

213: Breath-holding spells

214: Walkers

365 WAYS TO CALM YOUR CRYING BABY

215: The baby who wouldn't sleep

216: Donut on the head

217: The play yard: don'ts

218: The amazing flying baby

219: Ear infection, part 1

220: Ear infection, part 2

221: Ear infection, part 3

222: Nursing refusal

223: Diapering when there's a rash

224: Baby blasts

225: Ruining a good night's sleep

226: Just say no: sugar water

227: Performance art

228: Watch the honey, honey

229: Weaning

230: Telecommuting

231: Food rejection, part 1

232: Food rejection, part 2

233: The daily news

234: (C'mon baby, let's do) the twist

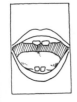

235: Teething, part 3

236: Just say no: sleeping with a bottle

237: Setting limits

238: Older sibs

239: Bring dad into the loop

240: Taking medicine

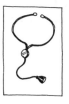

241: Croup

242: Mouth sores

243: Cellulitis

244: Burns

245: Bone or joint infections

246: Swollen lymph nodes

247: Intussusception

248: Toxic synovitis

12–24 Months: Toddlerhood

249: Exploration

250: Under cover

251: Sticker chart

252: Headphones

253: Going somewhere?

254: Finger guy

255: Baby videos

256: Soup

257: Round two goes to baby!

258: The crying playmate

259: Whining

260: Privacy

261: A night-light alternative

262: The way the cookie crumbles

263: Discipline

264: Enlist the help of friends—his friends!

265: Headache

266: Rubber stamp kit

267: Puzzles

268: Paint

269: Respect yourself

270: Sore throat

271: A play group

272: Mom's little helper

273: Constipation

 274: The library

 275: The long and winding road

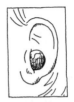 **276: Beads in the ear**

 **277: Pebble in the nose**

 278: Dust motes in the eye

 **279: Turn the tables**

 **280: Clinging**

 **281: Reschedule the toddler naptime**

 282: Herbal remedies

 283: The irregular toddler

 **284: The high-intensity toddler**

285: The negative toddler

286: The active toddler

287: The sensitive toddler

288: Milk allergy, part 2

289: Coping with distractions

290: Climbing falls

291: Whims

292: Fears

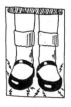

293: Poorly fitting shoes

294: Waking at night—again

295: Night terrors

296: Cuts

297: Giving up the bottle

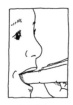

298: Molars

299: I'm outa here!

300: Yelling

301: Separation anxiety

302: Crying instead of talking

303: Lead colic

304: Crayons

305: Dancing

306: Battleground: the changing table

307: Bug bites

308: Use reverse psychology

309: Trading places

310: Animal bites

311: Security blankets and other objects

312: Good old Band-Aids

313: Understanding tantrums, part 1

314: Understanding tantrums, part 2

315: Let them settle it for themselves

316: Toddler's fracture

317: Splinters

318: "Use your words"

319: Taking turns

320: Battleground: the stroller

321: Cleaning the security blanket

322: Phone calls

323: "It's time to go"

324: TV, part 1

325: Battleground: dressing

326: "Tell me without crying"

327: Time-outs, part 1

328: Time-outs, part 2

329: Redirect the energy

330: Help is coming—soon

331: Make a promise you can keep

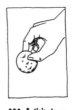

332: Anticipate an overload

333: "No" means "no"

334: "I know you're angry..."

335: Bring along the blankie

336: Bring the pillow, too

337: Spanking

338: Public tantrums

339: "Act like a big boy (or girl)"

340: "That's silly!"

341: Force-feeding

342: Dinnertime tantrums

343: Don't overbook his day

344: TV, part 2

345: Tantrums and allergies

346: Control their environment

347: Preparing an older sib for the new baby

348: Making medicine yummy

349: Another tip for giving medicine

350: Febrile seizures

351: Mouth injuries

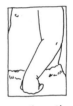

352: Nursemaid elbow

353: External ear infections

354: Sinusitis

355: Urinary tract infection (UTI)

356: Vaginitis

357: Balanitis and paraphimosis

358: Chicken pox

359: Go online

360: Hotlines

361: Magazines

362: Juicy poops

363: Hair pulling

364: How to use a crying baby

365: The final word

"A screaming comes across the sky"
—THOMAS PYNCHON, *Gravity's Rainbow*

Introduction

Like clockwork, at 2:00 A.M. every night, and then again shortly after 5:00 A.M., my one-month-old daughter Zoe's piercing cry would blast through my sleeping brain and nearly cause a convulsion.

My wife is a firm believer in breastfeeding, which meant that my job was relegated to merely diaper changing and then a swift handoff to my (also semiconscious) wife. But Zoe, for all her firepower, did not hold a candle to our first two boys, Alexander and Nathan. Now *there* were world class criers. Zoe's late-night assault on the hearing senses was nothing compared to the artillery barrage that was Alexander or the surprise, explosive guerrilla volleys that characterized Nathan's colic.

As a pediatrician, one who specializes in pediatric emergency medicine, and swaddled in the comfort of a wife who is an ex-NICU (Neonatal Intensive Care Unit) nurse, I never had the sort of fear that most other parents experience nightly. Namely, that all this excessive crying represented some dread malady or intolerable pain. All this crying is, we repeated endlessly to ourselves and each other, nothing more than a healthy exercise of lung power. The only ill effects were an unpleasant but temporary transformation from darling, beloved baby into fearsome, nocturnal creature the likes of whom would make Dracula think twice about the *après*-sun lifestyle. Our children were (are) possessed. Plain and simple.

Therefore, the task of compiling 365 ways to calm a crying baby comes naturally, almost effortlessly (okay, okay, the first 250 were easy, anyway). We have accumulated days, weeks, months, and years of management skills in soothing a crying baby (sometimes just in the course of one night!). And on those days when I'm not at home, I field anxious questions in the ER, often at 1 or 2 A.M., such as: "Are you sure there's nothing wrong with my baby?" "Do other babies cry like this?" "Are you SURE there's nothing wrong?" "What do *you* do when your baby cries?" "Are there any other doctors here?" (there are, but I'm the only pediatrician) and "Do you mean to tell me that all this crying is *normal* and there's *NOTHING WRONG* with my baby?" This is an invitation to settle in for a brief but focused seminar (time permitting, of course) on the wide world of colic. I tell them that crying is stressful, but only to parents, and try to identify what they have done in the past that calms the baby down. If it worked once, it might work again; and if not, I have lots of tips to pass on from previous ER middle-of-the-night parents. Most of the time, the baby has quieted down after a long wait, and the family goes home reassured that (1) their child is healthy, (2) they are not alone, and (3) one day *soon* this will all go away.

Why 365 ways? Why not just a couple? Doesn't that mean that they don't work? Of course these work. But there are a variety of reasons to supply a bounty of crying tips.

First, you must understand one very important thing about your baby: Crying is the language of babies, and all their needs have to be expressed within variations of pitch and intensity. Think of what you would do if you had to tell everyone what's on your mind without using words or gestures.

Secondly, with all the tons of books out there on general parenting and baby care, there is a dearth of books that specifically address what to do for crying and none that fit the how-to, hands-on approach taken here.

The eminent pediatrician T. Berry Brazelton best defines the "language" of crying. He describes six types of cries: pain, hunger, colic, boredom, discomfort, and letting-off-steam-at-the-end-of-the-day, and how to recognize each of these types of cry. "As time goes by, crying becomes clearer in its goals," says he. He's right. By recognizing your baby's needs and individual way of expressing himself, the job of managing his crying becomes that much easier. Much of what follows are ways to help you tune into those needs, expressions, or personality traits and figure out what your baby is saying to you by crying.

Another major theme throughout this book is reliance on your doctor. Your doctor can distinguish medical from nonmedical causes for crying, understands babies' behavioral and emotional needs, and has, presumably, fielded crying questions many, many times before. One note: In the following, references to your "doctor" means pediatrician, family practitioner or nurse practitioner, or NP. An NP has an advanced nursing degree for completion of a specific training program such as pediatrics. Nurse practitioners are, therefore, professionals who are thoroughly, extensively trained in handling routine pediatric problems. If your doctor's group uses nurse practitioners, rest assured that they are carefully selected, and hopefully you have already developed a trusting relationship with them.

Significant medical problems that cause crying are usually accompanied by other symptoms, but occasionally crying may be the first sign of trouble. When a medical cause seems to be the reason for crying, consult with your pediatrician or family physician for definitive guidance. Make sure you understand your instructions. It's very easy to go with the flow when dealing with a warm, fuzzy, people-oriented kid doctor. You don't want to waste their time with questions when they have a waiting room full of kids to see. But if you don't understand the purpose, dosage, or timing of a medication, you are doing your baby a disservice. You'll wind up calling the same doctor (or worse, a different doctor who does not know you or your baby) after hours for the same questions you had back when you were in the office.

Save the late-night calls for times when you really think there may be something wrong. If you're frustrated because your baby won't stop crying at 1:00 A.M., a call to your doctor might send the signal, due to the lateness of the hour, that you are worried about a major health problem. He may reflexively send you to the ER, which is no place to get meaningful help for a colicky baby. Persistent crying is difficult if not impossible to manage in an ER. There often is not enough time to evaluate the situation with the depth it deserves, and you may be forced to wait for hours only to be interrupted by a more urgent or acute problem when the doctor finally does show.

Speaking of emergencies, deciding when to go to an ER for an illness, injury, or poisoning is a tough call to make in many circumstances. In the ER, one of the questions I am most frequently asked is "Should we have come or not?" Some generalizations can be made, but when in doubt, always call your doctor first or, if they are unreachable or take an excessive amount of time to return your call, go to the ER if you are concerned about your baby's health.

Injuries that need to be treated right away include:

- Cuts that are so deep that you can see fat (yellow, popcornlike stuff).
- Cuts whose edges can be pulled apart.
- Inability to bear weight on a leg.
- Arm or leg deformity.
- Bruising and swelling that make it difficult to tell if there is a deformity.
- Head injuries with a loss of consciousness, vomiting, visual difficulties.
- Stomach injuries with vomiting and/or blood in the urine.
- Back injuries that produce weakness or numbness below the level of injury.

Symptoms of illness that deserve immediate attention include:

- Breathing problems that cause disorientation, blueness to the hands, lips, or feet.
- Stomachaches accompanied by high fevers, vomiting, and no appetite or worsening with food.
- A limp that develops with a fever when there has been no trauma.
- Any headache.
- Any persistent, unexplained pain.
- A previously known medical problem not responding to usual medications or treatments.

Most childhood poisonings are nontoxic. But that piece of information doesn't help you when you discover your toddler with his hand to his mouth and some unknown substance descending his esophagus. It is not until just such a moment that you wonder for the first time if _____ (fill in the blank: pencil erasers, adhesive tape, plant leaves, dog hair, etc.) is poisonous. The first thing to do: Call the local poison control center and tell them exactly what you saw or think you saw him take. Poison centers are staffed by professionals specially trained in toxicology; they have resources to tell you if there is an urgent problem or not. If it might be serious or if there is doubt about what was ingested, you will be directed to the nearest appropriate ER.

Finally, as a good rule of thumb, when you *do* get to the ER, call your insurance company to authorize the visit. If it ever is disputed, most arbitrators err on the side of the prudent layperson's assumption that an emergency existed at the time—but don't take any chances.

Both the causes and language of crying change as your baby grows and develops, so the book is divided into sections by age: 0–3 months, 3–12 months, and 12–24 months. Each entry is structured in roughly the same way, namely, identify the cause of the crying and offer a fun, helpful, imaginative response. In some cases all that is involved is seeing your baby-world in a new way; others require going out and buying something, doing something, or recruiting somebody. There are a number of products designed to soothe your baby's troubled cries and well-written books to help you understand one or another aspect of caring for your baby. I have done my best to identify the good ones. I do not offer any guarantees that they will work nor do I have any vested interest in the sales or success of any of these products. Just try 'em.

Coping with cabin fever was a major consideration in putting this book together. Don't take offense if some suggestions imply a degree of overdomestication. You *have* a baby at home, therefore you undoubtedly also have a household and need to spend a minimum effort each day on cooking, cleaning, and shopping. So if I sound like a broken record (take him into the kitchen with you…), it is only to expand the range of ways to incorporate your baby into the daily routines. While I'm on the high road, I also want to point out that this is not a sexist issue. Any dad who stays home with his child is bound to have these same issues as the mom who successfully manages a home, a baby, and a career all at the same time.

Finally, there may be times when a baby's wailing can be a distinct *advantage* to you. You'll get a seat on the bus or subway, get annoying telemarketers off the phone so much more easily, or move to the front of the grocery checkout line right away.

So good luck. You'll need it. Chances are, by the time this hits the shelves, Zoe will have outgrown her colic. But just think: By the time you finish reading this, maybe your baby will have outgrown hers, too.

0-3 MONTHS:
THE FIRST WEEKS
OF INFANCY

Learn her different cries

A change in the pitch of your baby's crying can be a sign of pain or serious illness. By the time your baby is even a few days old, you will be accustomed to the pitch, intensity, and volume of her cries. As she grows, you will be able to discriminate when the crying indicates differing needs or wants. When you hear a persistent piercing or shrieking cry, call your doctor. It may represent an infection of some kind or a subtle injury such as a hair tourniquet or corneal abrasion. (More on this later.)

TIP

1

Act now!

Those of you with older children may be used to letting your child have a few minutes to cry out whatever it is that's bothering her (this prospect will, undoubtedly, seem unimaginably cruel to first-timers). But this won't work for newborns, especially if you know that your baby can settle into a good, long hour or two of crying if she really sets her mind to it. Get into gear right away—*don't* wait before trying *something* to calm her down. Once she is in full crying mode, she won't remember what got her started in the first place. She's just crying with momentum after the first minute or two and will be much harder to soothe in the long run.

TIP

2

The rooting reflex

The "rooting" reflex is the name given to the inborn reflex whereby a baby turns her face toward the side on which her cheek is stroked. Presumably, it is a homing device so that a baby can latch on to a breast and feed. It is a powerful reflex, and you can initiate it simply by rubbing her cheek with a finger. This alone may stop a crying spell, but you will need to let her suck on your finger or breast or have a bottle ready if you do this (otherwise you're just teasing her).

This reflex persists until about eight to ten weeks of age. By then, baby's eyesight and hearing have developed to the point that she can take advantage of environmental stimuli to know when food is on the way.

TIP

3

The car

All young babies fall asleep in cars. It may be the vibration, the noise, the fresh air, a combination of these, or something else altogether. The important thing is that it works. When it is 2:30 in the morning and you *know* that the crying could go on for another hour, ask yourself which is worse—getting out of the house for a twenty-minute car trip or another hour of crying?

The choice should be easy.

TIP

4

Vibrating teddies

Baby won't really *play* with toys yet and won't for another few months, but in the first months, there are some toys that your baby will really respond to. They are ones that he can grasp himself.

One really effective, soothing toy is a vibrating teddy bear (or puppy or hippo). Several major manufacturers make them. Some babies respond to them because they simulate the sounds of their old uterine home, and some babies respond because they taste good when they suck on their ears (they are made of cloth, not fur, so you don't have to worry about hairs coming loose).

TIP

5

High-contrast mobiles

The foreign world of the newborn's mind is not nearly as impenetrable as you might think. A large number of neonatologists, developmentalists, behaviorists, neurologists, and neurobiologists, to name but a few, have devoted their lives to understanding the workings of the newborn baby's brain. One of the things that is now known is that babies have only a rudimentary sense of vision when they are born, but that it develops quickly.

Babies can distinguish between faces and seem to recognize their mother almost at birth. Beyond that, they "see" little more than bright and dark colors early on. This means that you might be able to distract their attention from crying by getting them to track a bright checkerboard or bull's-eye target.

These high-contrast patterns are almost a standard part of the discharge packet from hospitals. A truly worthwhile purchase is a mobile with high-contrast boards that attaches to your crib's side rail. Baby can look at the floating patterns and calm himself.

TIP

It's a snap

A Onesies' snap, that is. Every day, your little bundle of joy is a little bigger bundle than yesterday. And she will outgrow those tiny, cute little newborn outfits before she has had a chance to wear some of them even once. And the first time it hits you that your little peanut has grown is when she cries because her shirt is too tight, her snaps are pinching, or she's busting out of the armholes. Hopefully there's a supply of clothes the next size up from the one you *thought* you needed.

Clothes, of course, aren't the only things that pinch. A diaper may be too tight, panties or socks may be uncomfortable, or a hair ribbon may be pulling her hair. And this is a good place to make a safety pitch: Necklaces and bracelets are dangerous for babies. Save them at least for the terrible twos when she wants to dress up for her date with Prince Charming.

TIP

7

Swaddling

In the first few weeks of life, when your baby seems to exercise his lungs every waking moment, you'll often note an agitated sort of posturing, one arm shooting out in a fencing position, legs drawn up and kicking. These are primitive reflexes and disappear as your baby's motor development allows voluntary, controlled movements to replace reflexive ones. But until those go away, all this excess jerking around may be part of the crying problem, and he might be happier if he can stop thrashing around.

Swaddling in a blanket will eliminate the posturing and may help the crying in its own right. The way it's done in hospitals is as follows: Lay the blanket down point up, like a baseball diamond, then fold the top corner down. Fold the left side corner around baby, leaving the right arm free. Fold the bottom corner up, tucking the legs in; then finally wrap the right corner around the baby, snuggling the left arm into the bundle, tucking the corner into the top. Sort of like a baby-taco. Most babies like this kind of tight swaddling because it positions them as they were back in the "good ol' days" in the womb.

TIP

8

Warm the wipes

Changing a baby's diaper may not get you very far in settling her attitude if she is anticipating a cold, wet paper product being slapped against her bottom. Wipes are a wonderful thing: They don't dissolve or tear and they get the job done. But the cold is another matter.

You can't boil them, and you can't microwave them safely. (It creates hot spots.) Thank goodness someone invented Warm Wipes. This is a plug-in warmer that wraps around the standard wipes box and brings baby wipes to a more tolerable temperature.

TIP

9

Singing

Singing to baby when she is fussy may help her calm herself. She likes the sound of your voice, and rhythmic chanting or singing can lull her into a better or more receptive mood, to say nothing of the enhancement to language development. As you're cradling and rocking her, she will tune into you more thoroughly if you keep your voice modulated and soft and the song repetitive. If you try to drown her out, she will cry all the louder; if you soften your voice, she may quiet her crying down in order to hear you better.

You may get tired of hearing your own voice singing the same songs, but that is just what your child wants: the same reliable voice, singing the same reliable lullabies.

TIP

10

Live music

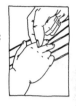

You can play music to lull your tired, cranky one to sleep without any kind of musical skill and without ever having taken a lesson in your life. "The Music Maker" is a zitherlike instrument that comes complete with songsheets that fit under the strings, indicating which notes to play. It can double as an interactive toy, and you can take your baby's hand to pluck the strings and have her create the music herself.

This product is available in stores and catalogs and was undoubtedly in your own toy chest when you were a child.

TIP

11

The stroller

Sometimes a long, bumpy stroller ride will calm down a fierce crying bout. If the sun is out, take the opportunity to see the world and go for that (probably) much-needed walk. If you absolutely *must*, bring a cell phone with you, but a break from that will probably do you good, too. (Grandma can catch up on news of her little woogums an hour later). With our oldest son, there were days when it was just too cold to bundle up and go outside. We would race the stroller down the main hallway of our townhouse, do a hairpin turn and race back the other way, first going the *left* way around the dining table, then the *right* way. This system mattered a great deal to him at the time, and although he denies it now, he must have had his reasons.

TIP

12

Drinking water

A baby who is exclusively breastfed does not *need* water. But there's nothing wrong with *offering* a bottle of water to a screaming baby. Colicky babies like to suck, and there may be times when breastfeeding just is not practical— for instance, ten minutes after he has last nursed. For whatever reason you choose, water is okay to offer the baby.

If you are breastfeeding, take advantage of this opportunity to bring dad into the loop. He will otherwise be deprived of the chance to participate in something very special: feeding his baby. It provides a good education for him, too. He'll learn that he can be just as successful as mom at controlling his baby's crying.

Your thumb

A crying baby likes to suck on things and will willingly suck on your thumb (or any other finger) if offered. Some babies latch on to a pinky and then hang on for dear life. You should, of course, carefully wash your hands with soap and hot water beforehand. Once clean, there are no greater or fewer bacteria on your fingers than on the breast of a nursing mother.

Then just try and pry your finger away! (There's nothing kinky about admitting that it feels kind of nice, either.)

TIP

14

Get out the burps, part 1

Feeding, whether from a bottle or breast, is accompanied by swallowing a lot of air. Crying adds more air. Baby's little belly only has so much room, and it won't hold both food and air. (Two guesses as to which one is more nutritionally sound.) To *avoid* crying due to excess stomach air, burp him every five minutes or so while feeding. If he is quick to cry and quick to feed, go the distance and save burping for when he takes a pause. It is the worrier-type baby who grunts and fusses while nursing who is most likely to need a good burping in the middle of a meal.

TIP

15

Swing time

I don't know how we would have made it through our oldest son's colic without a swing. (I don't know how we made it through, period.) All the major manufacturers of children's toys, Fisher Price, PlaySkool, etc., make safe, durable swings. They rest on four legs, have a bucket seat with a lap belt, and recent models have *silent* manual or battery-powered winders.

If nothing else was working when Alexander was crying, we would just put him in his swing; and sometimes all it took to settle him down to sleep was the rhythmic back and forth swinging. If he was quieting but not truly heading for sleep, we would sometimes noisily rewind the spring, and he actually liked that part of it, too.

The swings last forever. If you don't have one, get one secondhand from a neighbor or a yard sale. This should be standard equipment in any baby-ready house.

TIP

16

Song: "Over in the Meadow"

A ll three of my children have gone to sleep, thanks to the patience of my wife, over the years with this one song.

Over in the meadow, in the sand, in the sun
Lived an old mother frog and her little froggie one.
Croak! said the mother, I croak, said the one,
So they croaked and were happy in the sand,
    in the sun.

Over in the meadow, in the pond so blue,
Lived an old mother fish and her little fishies two.
Swim! said the mother, We swim, said the two,
So they swam and were happy in the pond so blue.

Over in the meadow, in the nest in the tree,
Lived an old mother bird and her little birdies three.
Sing! said the mother, We sing, said the three,
So they sang and were happy in the nest in the tree.

TIP

17

Rocking chair

You did not automatically sign up to become a marathon walker when you had your baby. Although pacing back and forth with a colicky baby seems to be a predestined fate, you can actually accomplish the daunting task of jiggling or patting him into a quieter mood during a colic fit with your feet up in a rocking chair or glider (which is a rocker that glides back and forth on a standing base).

Some babies seem to respond to the swinglike sensation alone. If so, try this: Rest the baby on her belly on the glider while you kneel at her side. Put your hand on her back and rock her back and forth in the chair while softly singing a favorite song. *Never* leave her on a glider unattended.

Gliders also make for a good place to nurse or read to her, not to mention a comfy place for *you* to take a nap.

I'm just bored

Ｉt starts early.

It may take all of your time and energy to get your darling baby fed, changed, bathed, burped, and off to naptime. You finally have a few minutes to yourself, and then it happens. A whimper. A cry. A more forceful bellow. She napped for all of ten minutes and now she's up again. You go to her bassinet, and what do you find? A big, bright smile!

Starting as early as six or eight weeks, your baby begins to start saying she just wants to be held and be with mommy (or daddy). If she's all alone in bed, she gets bored. She knows that her crying works for just about every other need she has, so why not use it when all she wants is a companion?

It is frustrating to give up your "free" time when she wants to play during her naptime. You may need to adjust your notion of when baby's naptime occurs, since your baby may have adjusted *her* notion of when to nap. But this is one of the big rewards of parenting: She loves you and wants you to play with her.

TIP

19

Lambskin rug

A baby present that won't get discarded after a single wear or stored away until she's much older is a lambskin rug. There is nothing more soothing or luscious than a lambskin rug against baby's back or belly. Use it as a place to change her diaper or cuddle her with it wrapped around her, and you should see instant results.

Running water

There's no real explanation for why this works, but some babies are just captivated by the sound and look of running water. And as long as you can arrest their attention, they may forget to cry. Run the water in the tub. Have him watch it to calm down before he goes in for a bath, or run it in the sink and have it splashing on dishes and pans so he can watch the spray.

A fair notice: Be prepared to change the diaper. After all, the same instinct that makes *you* suddenly need to pee when you hear running water (and I'm not sure that modern— or even ancient—medicine has provided a good explanation for this) also hits your baby. So just make sure that you and your baby both have an empty bladder before trying this.

TIP

21

Song: "Nobody Likes Me"

This song is dedicated to the tired, frustrated baby who wants you to feel sorry for him.

Nobody likes me
Ev'rybody hates me
Guess I'll go eat worms
Long, thin, slimy ones
Short, fat, juicy ones
Itsy, bitsy, fuzzy, wuzzy worms.

Down goes the first one
Down goes the second one
Oh, how they wiggle and squirm
Long, thin, slimy ones
Short, fat, juicy ones
Itsy, bitsy, fuzzy, wuzzy worms.

Up comes the first one
Up comes the second one
Oh, how they wiggle and squirm
Long, thin, slimy ones
Short, fat, juicy ones,
Itsy, bitsy, fuzzy, wuzzy worms.

TIP

Music box

The tinkly, treacly sound of a music box may not be your cup of tea, especially after the fortieth or fiftieth replaying, but ask yourself this: Which is worse? Your baby's cries or "Here Come the Clowns?" for half an hour. If you know that your baby likes the tune and watching the porcelain clown turn slowly, go ahead and rewind it. Nothing, they say, (whoever '"they" are, and "they" always know best, don't "they"?) succeeds like success. Even if you have to drive yourself crazy with the same song over and over (which is why you may find yourself thinking in grammatically difficult, Winnie the Pooh-like, convoluted sentences that somehow or other do end up in the right place, after all!).

Have a supply of music boxes and toys around. In time, these items will serve as very special reminders of your teenager's precious first few months.

TIP
23

Stationary bicycle ride

Shpilkes. It's a Yiddish term, and it means "ants in the pants." If you are afflicted by shpilkes because you are used to exercising on a regular basis only to be derailed by a constantly colicky baby *and* the forces of nature have turned the weather against you as well, ride a stationary bike with your baby snuggled into a front carrier. An athletic dad who I know was able to clock fifteen- to twenty-mile rides this way—with his colicky baby girl purring contentedly away the entire time.

She would, he reports, cry immediately as soon as he got *off* the bicycle, thus providing a perfect excuse to keep on exercising.

And consider this: When springtime finally arrives, you'll be set to transfer baby (once she's old enough) to a trailer or a baby seat and keep up your riding habits.

TIP

24

Carry her!

When baby is crying with full force, the first thing you should always do is pick her up. Of course! The close warmth, familiar smell, and soft touch of your skin is very important to her and sends her very important signals about what is happening: that mommy or daddy is coming to the rescue. With time and luck, you will discover what carrying and rocking position your child likes best. Here are some to try:

- Face down, head in your hand.*
- Face down, head inside your elbow.
- Face down, over your shoulder.
- On her back, held against your body.
- Over your lap, on her tummy.

* When the baby is face down, you can support her head by resting her cheek in your hand or by cupping her chin between thumb and forefinger.

To poop or not to poop?

An infant may not have a bowel movement every day. This is *not* constipation. If pain does occur with infrequent bowel movements and causes crying, add a little sugar water to the baby's feeding. (A breastfed infant who is too young for a bottle can have it via a spoon or large eyedropper.) On rare occasions, it may be appropriate to try glycerine suppositories or a greased thermometer if, for example, baby grunts or cries to pass small, hard, pebbly poops. In general, your contact with your baby's rear end should be restricted to changing diapers and the occasional tickle.

Bowel habits are the source of intense emotion, philosophizing, and endless discussion. The baby's overall health and character are often needlessly called into question, and frequently the satisfaction of the parents' own bowel movements (or lack thereof) figures into their interpretation of *baby's* poops. As a good rule of thumb: Always assume that your baby's bowel movements are normal and that the consistency, frequency, and color of your baby's poop is just what it should be.

TIP

26

You can't spoil a baby

It may not seem like a good idea to get a baby used to the idea that you will respond to him every time he opens his mouth or makes an unhappy face, but it *is*. (By the way, does it seem as though every waking moment of your day is devoted to your baby's endless needs? It's not. It's actually every moment of your day *and* night.) You may worry that this is how babies get "spoiled" and that your baby will never accept any lesser degree of attention. *Don't* worry, it's not.

There are discrete stages of emotional growth, and the first one is learning the basis of trust. A baby learns to trust his parents in the first months of life each time they meet his essential needs: food, warmth, comfort. Your baby gains a valuable building block of "personhood" by your tending so lovingly to his needs. Such attention and caring, makes it easier to build trusting relationships with the other children and adults he will meet.

TIP

Song: "Michael Finnegan"

A pep-me-up song for a baby who's just coming up from a nap.

There was an old man named Michael Finnegan
He had whiskers on his chinnegan
They fell out and then grew in again
Poor old Michael Finnegan
Begin again.

There was an old man named Michael Finnegan
He went fishing with a pinnegan
Caught a fish and dropped it in again
Poor old Michael Finnegan
Begin again.

There was an old man named Michael Finnegan
He grew fat and then grew thin again
Then he died and had to begin again
Poor old Michael Finnegan
Begin again.

TIP

28

Sensory overload, part 1

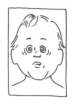

It happens inevitably: Everyone is over at your home, looking at your new baby, delivering presents and food, cooing excitedly at her. All of a sudden your placid, peaceful baby has a meltdown—screaming and wailing inconsolably. You feel terrible because your baby is so unhappy and fear that you'll never settle into a normal life with *adult* company ever again. Some babies do very badly in noisy, confusing, fast-changing situations. In order to tune it out, she may feel like she has to drown it out.

The solution lies in tailoring visits to times when your baby tends to be less cranky. The morning and early afternoon works best for most babies and, possibly, limiting the number of visitors or the number of times you let her get passed from friend to friend. They are more likely to go with the flow than at times when they are already overloaded from a full day of sights and sounds.

TIP

Sensory overload, part 2

Chaos can also descend on a house in the late afternoon as a matter of daily routine. Older kids come home from school, spouses arrive home from work, and a quiet household can erupt into Mount St. Helens.

This situation is easily amenable to change. Limit the sensory overload of having your children jiggle and bounce baby around. If the kids are playing noisily or enjoying loud TV or music, have them do it somewhere where it won't disturb the baby. This is the time of day when most babies go into their tailspin. A little preemptive planning can minimize late-afternoon screaming jags.

If there's simply no room to shunt the older kids to, see if an afterschool playdate can be arranged—once or twice a week. When dad arrives home, tell him to tone down the roughhousing (or in dire straits—have him work a little later at the office).

White noise tapes

Whether it is the noise or the motion, running the vacuum or taking baby for a car ride does seem to help. You can reproduce white noise without turning on energy-hungry appliances by purchasing CDs or tapes that play a soothing *hisss* of white noise. Certain dads may have trouble with this concept and will insist that if their baby is to listen to anything at all, they will listen to the good stuff (and the good stuff ranges from Bach to the Beatles to the Ramones), swearing by its inherent therapeutic value. Whatever.

Two recordings are: "Smart Baby's Colic Stop" (1-888-STOPCRY) and "For Crying Out Loud!" (1-800-548-8531).

CD player broken? Turn on the AM radio *between* two stations for the same effect—for free.

TIP

31

Feed him!

You've just fed your baby, and he's still crying. He seems to have eaten enough for a baby horse. Is it possible he's still hungry? Of course it is. Whether you're bottle feeding ("But he took three ounces at once yesterday and that was enough to satisfy him!") or nursing him ("He's been snacking all day!"), there is no guarantee that your baby has had enough to eat. Your baby is growing, and what may have filled him up just one or two days ago (or even one or two feedings ago) just may not be enough for him right now. If you want to see consistent eating habits in a family member, look to your husband instead.

Check the diaper—again?!

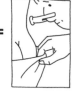

Day follows night, ducklings follow mother ducks, a rainbow follows a storm, New Yorkers follow the Knicks. A wet and poopy diaper can follow a feeding, a nap, a burp, just about anything. A quick hand to the bottom is usually all that is needed to solve this basic problem in baby maintenance.

Want to make your husband feel *great*?* Tell him you've been trying for *hours* to calm the baby, and now it's his turn. Place her in his hands, diaper first, and if he's good, he'll realize right away what needs to be done. Then, with an air of satisfaction generally only reserved for epochal male problem-solving events ("Honey, I found the remote!"), he'll hand her back to you, calm, smiling, and playful (the baby, that is), with the proud statement "She just needed a change, honey. And by the way, you look *great* for just having had a baby."

* This only works for a week or two. After that, you'll have to resort to good old reliable whining and begging.

TIP

33

Sleep

Waking from sleep is a perfectly natural phenomenon in the first few weeks, and the appropriate response is to feed and change him. A baby's circadian rhythm, the internal clock that tells us (most of us, anyway) to sleep and wake at regular intervals, won't be fully developed until six weeks at the earliest, often not until twelve to fifteen weeks in a breast-fed baby. In a newborn, feeding every two or three hours is normal, meets their physiological needs, and avoids hypoglycemia. A longer sleep period sets in by two months or when baby reaches a magic weight of about thirteen pounds. Thereafter, waking up in the middle of the night may have a number of problematic causes, some more intractable than others.

TIP

Song: "Clap Your Hands"

A snuggle-play song. Clap baby's hands, feet, and gently raise baby's arms in the air as you sing.

If you're happy and you know it, clap your hands
If you're happy and you know it, clap your hands
If you're happy and you know it, and you really
*   want to show it*
If you're happy and you know it, clap your hands.

If you're happy and you know it, stomp your feet
If you're happy and you know it, stomp your feet
If you're happy and you know it, and you really
*   want to show it*
If you're happy and you know it, stomp your feet.

If you're happy and you know it, shout Hurray!
If you're happy and you know it, shout Hurray!
If you're happy and you know it, and you really
*   want to show it*
If you're happy and you know it, shout Hurray!

TIP

Warm her up!

Your baby feels the same temperature as you do and reacts to it just the same, too. If you're wearing a wool sweater and your baby only has on a Onesies and the cute little dress your sister-in-law sent you, maybe your baby is crying because she's too cold.

The big difference between you and your baby, in terms of temperature control (or thermoregulation) is that baby loses and absorbs the greatest amount of heat through her head. Therefore, covering the head offers the best protection from the cold. If you feel cold, your baby needs to wear a hat. While you're at it, throw in a blanket to swaddle her in.

Cool him down!

It's January. It's cold out. When you came in from outside and your little guy was napping, you probably left him in his snowsuit, hat, blanket, and the three layers of wool he was wearing underneath, right? When he wakes up, he'll be sweaty, a clue to overbundling, and he may even have a fever. If he feels like he has a fever, take his temperature. If it's 101°F or less, remove all his clothing layers except for the Onesies and outfit, and recheck his temperature in fifteen to twenty minutes (do not give Tylenol or Motrin). The temperature should be normal and he'll be happy again. If the temperature persists, call your doctor.

Give her a cuddle

More than anything else she will ever need, your baby needs your love. In return, she will give you her love. The first, biggest milestone you will achieve as a parent (after giving birth, that is) is when your little girl stops crying and smiles at you—just because you showed up. This is her first way of saying that she loves you (other, more complicated, and sometimes paradoxical ways of expressing love come later). It is never too soon to expect that some of her cries are designed to get the comfort of being held by the one she loves.

At-home dad

Can a dad calm a crying baby just as effectively as a mom? Yes, but he may, at first, feel like a fish out of water and need a little more help. A vital fact that may not be obvious to dads—but moms know this—is that you're not alone. Just as mom thrives on the company of other moms who are suffering the same headaches from sleep deprivation, you too may benefit in knowing that there are other fathers who are going through the same uncertainties and tentative victories as you. There is even a newsletter for stay-at-home dads. It's called *At Home Dad*. Write to 61 Brightwood Ave., North Andover, MA, 01845 ($12/year for a quarterly subscription).

TIP

39

Colic, part 1

The word *colic* is a general term, derived from the Greek *kolikos*, relating to the colon, and is defined as "spasmodic pains in the abdomen," although there is no evidence that colic really is caused by abdominal disorders. Infantile colic is characterized by episodes of inconsolable screaming, lasting for several hours, and typically occurring at a specific time of day. It affects about 20 percent of all infants. The baby is flushed, with arms and legs tightly flexed, often passing gas, probably a result of swallowed air and overexercised abdominal muscles. It often begins at age two or three weeks, maxes out at about six weeks, and may last until the third or even fourth month.

TIP

40

Colic, part 2

Infantile colic is *not* rigidly defined. It is not a specific condition, like appendicitis or pneumonia, that can be accurately diagnosed and, more importantly, specifically treated. There is no known physical or emotional cause for colic, although theories abound. Some of the more commonly held notions about colic will be discussed from place to place in this book.

Above all, try to keep this one point firmly in mind throughout your ordeal: Colic is *not* an illness. Your baby is healthy. Sick babies are limp, pale, and quiet. They are not vigorous, red, and fighting mad. Dr. T. Berry Brazelton, the preeminent pediatrician for our generation, thinks that babies cry so hard as part of an effort to tune out an overwhelming environment after hours of trying to assimilate it all.

A couple of helpful references are: *Touchpoints*, T. Berry Brazelton, M.D. (Addison-Wesley) and *Cry Babies, Coping with Colic: What to do when your baby won't stop crying* by Mark Weissbluth, M.D. (Berkeley Press).

TIP

Sing her praises

This one takes a long time to really help crying, but you can't ignore it: Make up a song using her name and sing it to her when you are changing or carrying or strolling her. This worked like a charm for our daughter. My wife sang to her:

> *Zoe is a little bitty fish,*
> *A little bitty fish,*
> *A little bitty fish.*
> *Zoe is a little bitty fish,*
> *Swimming in the sea.*

The reason this takes so long, of course, is that it will take a long time for her to understand that the sound of her name actually means *her.* (You also teach her, her name by playing peekaboo games. ("Where's Zoe? I see Zoe!") But once she does get it, you've got a great tool to always get her attention. And then you'll be ready to make up newer and sillier songs using her name.

TIP

42

The football hold

Oh, baby, do some kids love this! Place your baby face down on your left forearm (vice versa for lefties), with his chin supported by your hand and his legs straddling your elbow. This puts you two in the perfect position for a variety of things:

- Pat him on the back with your right hand.
- Stroke his back briskly.
- Gently rock him back and forth with your left arm.
- Gently bounce him up and down with your left arm.
- The end run: Right arm in front to ward off defense, feet carefully picking out obstacles, run with him from your family room to your bedroom. (Don't do a war whoop and toss the ball/baby when you get the touchdown.)

TIP

Neck nuzzling

Snuggled into your neck, your crying baby will discover a world of comforts:

- Your chin will probably cover his entire head (a source of warmth).
- Hum, and your throat will vibrate.
- Dad's six o'clock (make that ten o'clock, usually) shadow may be soothing.
- Resting his tummy across your chest may put him in tune with the slow, deep rhythm of breathing and the soft thump of your heartbeat.

TIP

44

Fight the gas

Colicky babies seem to pass an excessive amount of gas. As far as can be clinically determined, though, colicky babies are no more "gassy" than non-colicky babies. Therefore, trying to relieve a baby's gas should not really help matters. However, one of the most common pieces of advice given by well-meaning friends and relatives is to try simethicone (Mylicon, Phazyme). This is an anti-gas medication that is not absorbed by the intestinal tract and is often used by adults for bloating or gas. It is completely safe for babies and has no side effects. It may help a little bit, a lot, or not at all. This is *not* likely to globally change the pattern of fierce, constant crying; but if it helps, keep it in your arsenal.

TIP

45

"Calming" overload

The quiet, placid baby who develops colicky crying and then gets even *more* agitated when you try rocking, singing, and gentle patting may be experiencing "calming" overload. He may not need three things going on at once to calm himself down. A low-key baby who thrives on a placid environment may do better with only gentle rhythmic patting without the singing or a white-noise tape playing in the background.

Backing off is against the grain of most advice you usually get, which tends to be "try doing this next if you haven't already." Some babies don't like a lot of fuss.

TIP

46

Coo and carry

Carrying alone just may not cut it with some colicky criers. Some babies demand a whole repertoire of moves and acts on your part before they will settle down. She may like to be gently patted on the back, on the bottom, on the chest, etc. Some babies like to be patted a little more forcefully, like polite clapping. If you are standing, swaying from side to side might help calm her. Then, while holding, clapping, and swaying, try humming softly in her ear "aah-aah bay-BEE! aah-aah bay-BEE!" Keep this up for a few minutes if it seems to be working, and your baby will get into the rhythm and begin to calm down. In time your baby will anticipate the rhythm and *that* will help her calm down, too.

TIP

Song: "Alice the Camel"

"Alice the Camel" is a good nuzzling song. Rhythmic, repetitive songs such as this work best once you've got a baby crying in a rhythm and you need to wind her down to sleep. (To the tune of "One Little, Two Little, Three Little Indians")

Alice the camel has five humps.
Alice the camel has five humps.
Alice the camel has five humps.
So go, Alice, go.

Alice the camel has four humps.
Alice the camel has four humps.
Alice the camel has four humps.
So go, Alice, go.

Alice the camel has three humps.
Alice the camel has three humps.
Alice the camel has three humps.
So go, Alice, go.

Sing each verse again as:

TIP

Alice the camel has two humps;
Alice the camel has one hump;
Alice the camel has no humps (but last line
    change to: *Now Alice is a horse*).

48

Don't even think about it: Shaking

No matter how frustrated you are with your baby, *don't* ever shake him/her in a moment of anger. Your baby will not suddenly understand that you are serious in your desire for him to stop crying nor will he be "afraid" to cry in front of you any longer. He will just get even more agitated. Put him down and let him cry if you have to get away from him—that is far preferable to losing control. The crying won't hurt him, and shaking a baby can cause permanent, irreparable brain damage. Don't be afraid to recognize that you have come close to losing control. Many parents of screaming infants get very distraught in just the same circumstances. There are hotlines to help you at just such a moment, such as the Parental Stress Hotline (800-632-8188). Call them if you are at your wit's end—that's why they are there.

TIP

49

Give in to the colic

The baby is the one with the colic. It is as much a part of his being as his birth weight or having five fingers on each hand. Colic is not a response to parental diet, mood, anxiety, or a bear market. It is not a health problem, allergy, intestinal disorder, or "exercising" the lungs. It is purely a phenomenon of infancy, not a portent of personality types or problems to come. In short, it's just an excessive amount of crying.

Despite all of the other 364 suggestions in this book, there may be times—maybe just for half an hour a day—when the best way to manage your baby's colic is to just let him cry. After all, if Brazelton is correct, it serves him a useful purpose, and you'll feel better knowing he's really okay when he does settle himself down. If people ask you why your baby is crying, you can simply say, "He has colic." If they ask, "Aren't you worried?" your answer can be, "No, just tired and headachy."

TIP

50

Off schedule

Conflicts don't wait until adolescence to appear. *You* may have decided to put him on a schedule where he naps twice a day and sleeps through the night, but this may not sit well with him. He may have other ideas.

Some babies thrive best on a set, ironclad schedule and don't want it to be changed. When they get off schedule, they become cranky and inconsolable.

There *are* ways to change a baby's schedule when it does not work for you. If you are trying to eliminate a 1:00 A.M. feeding, shorten it bit by bit each night or move it ahead five or ten minutes each night. Skip the diaper change to minimize stimulation, if you can. Minimize cooing or singing during the feeding. Eventually he will give it up, and you will be able to establish the schedule you want. Just take baby steps.

TIP

Get out the burps, part 2

Some babies burp easily, others put you through a great deal of contortions. Some like rubbing, others like clapping or patting. You may need to mix'n'match. It may feel like no position works reliably, but whatever works for *your* baby is the right method. Try these:

- Rub his back, then pat him a few times.
- Firmly clap his back while he's over your shoulder.
- Clap his back while he is lying on your lap, stomach down.
- Rub his belly while he is sitting upright on your lap.
- To any of the above, add a little side-to-side swaying.

Once a baby has been crying for a while, he is sure to have added to his woes by swallowing an uncomfortable amount of air. A good burp in the midst of a crying fit may help him start the process of getting calm once again.

TIP

52

The miracle reflex

Once your baby begins to settle down (and this works great in conjunction with the pacifier), stroke her forehead lightly, right down the middle, to the bridge of her nose. This stimulates a reflex to close her eyes, and she will immediately take a slow, deep breath. Do it a couple of times and you may break the crying fit, or at least slow it. With a little luck, she will fall asleep. This reflex is present until about two months of age.

TIP

53

The dishwasher

Kill two birds with one stone. Put your tough guy in his favorite seat (bouncy seat, car seat—anything as long as it is secure) on top of the dishwasher, washer, or dryer and turn it on full force. The same vibration that makes a car ride so successful in managing colic may help to calm him down. Chances are, you will probably need to sing to him, use a pacifier, and maybe even pat him on his belly. A safety tip: Stay close by and make sure that the vibration of the machine cannot slide the seat over the edge. If the seat does start to drift—set the machine to a lower power level.

TIP

54

Puppets

Just like a tape of your voice is guaranteed to grab your baby's attention, a little puppet play can soothe her like a charm. Buy a few colorful puppets and create a couple of funny voices. Themes that a baby is likely to respond to include social situations and mommy-baby games that she experiences every day. Try this:

Elephant (left hand puppet, grumpy voice): *Hi, Mrs. Winnipissaukee! I want to play with your baby.*

Mrs. Winnipissaukee (right hand puppet, squeaky voice): *Come in, Mr. Elephant! Baby Jujube is sleeping, so don't wake her up with your big trunk!*

Elephant: (Lets out a loud wail with his trunk.)

Mrs. Winnipissaukee: *Silly elephant! I told you that would make the baby laugh.*

TIP

55

The trick to transferring

In our household, the rule is "You wake him, you get him back to sleep." The last thing any parent wants to do is wake a sleeping baby. So rather than unstrap baby from the car seat and gingerly place him in his stroller, it is far easier to put the whole thing, baby and car seat, in the stroller itself. Then the bumpy stroller ride keeps him asleep. You can buy a car seat/stroller combo, and some strollers are designed specifically to accommodate the most common car seat models. Check the Katie's Kids catalog (1-847-615-2478) or The Right Start (800-548-8531).

Enjoy this feature while you can—all too soon your baby will be in a "big kids" car seat, which is too large and heavy to put in any stroller.

TIP

56

Change the formula

Your baby was born with a unique personality, and that includes specific likes and dislikes. The formula you're feeding him just may not appeal to him, and he may cry when he tastes it (although a strong preference for the taste of one formula over another at *this* age can be a sign of a strong temperament and other strong opinions to come). You have nothing to lose by changing formulas if he prefers one to another, as they all are nutritionally complete for babies. Keep in mind that you should stay within formula types (i.e., Similac, Enfamil, and SMA are all "regular," cow's milk–based formulas, and Prosobee, Isomil, and Nursoy are soy-based formulas). It may be reasonable to switch from a regular formula to a soy formula, but consult your doctor first.

If changing formula doesn't work or the effect seems to have worn off after a few days, don't despair. Try another formula, and alternate between those that provide relief. If nothing seems to help after one or two switches, forget it, and stick to the original formula.

TIP

Roll out the great books

By "great" I mean great in the literal sense—massive, huge, voluminous. James Joyce's *Ulysses*, Thomas Pynchon's *Gravity's Rainbow*, Tolstoy's *Anna Karenina*,—or the Manhattan Yellow Pages.

Rifle the pages right in front of the baby, creating both a light breeze and a gentle buzzing sound. The breeze itself may prompt a reflexively inhaled breath (see #53); and if that doesn't work, you can always try reading the book to him and *boring* him to sleep. By age six to eight months, your baby will become sufficiently interested in literature for its own sake—and tear the pages out of the book in order to eat them. Which is what critics meant by the phrase "tastefully written."

TIP

58

Leg exercise

A tummy full of gas is normal for a baby—any baby, every baby. There's no way to avoid it—they swallow air with every feeding and every crying spell. But if your baby seems to have more than his fair share of gas, gently exercising his legs back and forth to work out the gas may offer some relief.

Put the baby down on his back, hold a leg in each arm, and work each leg up and down, just like riding a bicycle. Keep going at it for at least five to ten minutes at a time. Massage the muscles in his thighs, calves, and feet while you're at it. This will stir his belly up and may relieve him of some crampy, distending air. Or it may have no effect on the gas whatsoever, but he may enjoy the massage and calm down anyway.

TIP

Bathtime

Bathing (especially once baby has graduated from sponge baths) is as close as it gets to a surefire method to stop crying. The cool air may cause even more crying as he is being undressed, but as soon as he gets into comfortably warm water, his attitude should improve. Use a washcloth or your hands to gently wet and soap him. Either way should make him feel cozy and content. It is probably best to not shampoo his hair until he has settled down significantly, to avoid getting soap and water into his eyes, nose, and/or mouth. Have a soft towel immediately at hand to wrap him in to minimize that transition back to the cooler air.

(Should you be so unlucky to have a baby who actually *hates* his bath, all of the foregoing will sound like the ravings of a lunatic.)

TIP

60

Koala walk

If your baby's screaming gets too intense, go outside. The air will seem fresher, and if there are pets or smokers at home, it actually *will* be fresher. His cries won't reverberate so loudly outdoors, either. Day or night, it doesn't really matter. Put him in a front carrier or just hold him. The warmth and closeness of your body should help him feel cozy and calm him down. Just like a koala bear would.

Don't make excuses for the weather if you can avoid it. If it's cold, bundle him up. If it's rainy, use the front carrier and take an umbrella. The walk will do you good, and it sets a great example for your baby.

TIP

61

Song: "The Eensy Weensy Spider"

This requires hand signals, so it works best when you're jiggling or resting baby in your lap. Alexander, our oldest boy homed in on this and settled down like he was under a hypnotist's spell.

The eensy weensy spider (pinch thumb and
   forefingers of both hands together)
Crawled up the water spout (as above, walk
   fingers up to your face)
Down came the rain (flutter all fingers of both
   hands down to your lap)
And washed the spider out (hands fly to both sides)
Out came the sun (both hands make arcs)
And dried up all the rain (wiggle fingers)
And the eensy weensy spider (repeat finger pinch
   and climb)
Crawled up the spout again.

TIP

Song: "Glunk, Glunk, Glunk"

I found this little gem on a Web site called Lullabies and Other Songs for Children (http://www.stairway.org/kidsongs/index.htm l). I have no idea what the tune is. Make one up.

"Barump," went the little green frog
"Barump," went the little green frog
"Barump," went the little green frog one day
And his eyes went, "Glunk, glunk, glunk!"

TIP

63

Start a ritual

Some babies thrive on rituals, and you can take advantage of this. If you respond to crying the same way each time (say, a little rocking, carrying, reading, and singing, followed by placing him in a stroller and going for a walk), he may quickly learn to expect what's coming and take comfort in the start of the routine.

It's never too early to learn your child's personality. He's born with it and expresses it much sooner than you realize. This intimate knowledge is a building block: for you as a parent, and for your baby to forge the bonds of trust and love.

TIP

64

Look: I have a thumb!

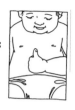

A major turning point of a baby's life is when he can begin to meet his own needs. At about six to eight weeks, he may discover that when his thumb appears in his mouth, it's because his thumb is attached to his arm, which is part of his body. If your baby pacifies himself with his own thumb, he should be encouraged to do so, despite what grandma may tell you. It is, when you think about it, his first chance to learn success. In time, he will give it up, probably in a few months, in favor of other exciting items to place in his mouth. Thumb-sucking that occurs later on in childhood does have undesirable consequences.

TIP

65

Toys, part 1

The primary considerations in choosing toys for your baby at any age are: Is it safe? Is it age-appropriate? Will she have fun with it?

Give her something to play with if she is crying from boredom. If she has just eaten, has a dry diaper, and is well rested, she might want to look at something fun. A shrieking, overstimulated baby probably has no use for a toy.

At this age, your baby needs brightly colored, high-contrast toys that she can bat her hands at, grasp, and/or shake. Often, baby seats are equipped with a row of toys that can be placed within reach. These serve to distract her attention and provide opportunities to improve eye-hand coordination. Toys that click, rattle, or have a bell are also good distractions and can hold her attention for brief periods.

TIP

66

Toys, part 2

Toys, such as rattles or sharp-contrast pictures, are good at drawing a baby's attention onto something other than his own tummy or his diaper at about six weeks old. But they only help for all of two to four minutes at a time. *Don't* expect that a toy will allow you more than a small window of time to separate his warring older siblings or collect your wits before going on to the next baby-related challenge. As baby gets older, a toy will be a more effective baby-sitter for longer periods of time.

TIP

Just say no: Tobacco

Cigarette smoke—or any other kind of smoke—may contribute to colicky crying. Definitive evidence of this may be years in coming, if ever, but it does not pay to wait for ironclad proof. Smoking *is* known to be irritating to your baby's throat and lungs and increases the risk of asthma and bronchitis later on from secondhand smoke. If you can't quit, take it outside. *Don't* allow friends or relatives to smoke in the house, either. It's a habit you probably do not want to pass on to your child; and the less she sees you doing it now, the less likely she will be inclined to smoke later.

TIP

68

Song: "Hush, Little Baby"

This is supposedly a southern lullaby. I'm not so sure. I'm from New York, my wife's from Jersey (*New* Jersey, for those of you who don't live in The City), and we both like to sing it to our kids. I include it here because, if you're like me, the lyrics are tough to remember after "diamond ring."

Hush, little baby, don't say a word,
Mama's gonna buy you a mockingbird.
And if that mockingbird don't sing,
Mama's gonna buy you a diamond ring.
And if that diamond ring turns brass,
Mama's gonna buy you a looking glass.
And if that looking glass gets broke,
Mama's gonna buy you a billy goat.
And if that billy goat won't pull,
Mama's gonna buy you a cart and bull.
And if that cart and bull turn over,
Mama's gonna buy you a dog named Rover.
And if that dog named Rover won't bark,
Mama's gonna buy you a horse and cart.
And if that horse and cart fall down,
You'll still be the sweetest little baby in town.

TIP

69

Song: "Keemo Kymo"

This is another song from the Lullaby home page. It's a song from Kentucky, but no tune is indicated. Make one up; the tune is less important than the rhythm. That's the main thing that will help soothe your baby.

There was a frog lived in a spring
Sing song kitty catch-a ky-mee-oh
He could dance and he could sing
Sing song kitty catcha kymee-oh

Keemo kymo dayro dime
Hey, ho, subble bubble sipso
Periwinkle soapfat, pennywinkle nip cat
Kitty catcha kymee-oh

Oh, what you gonna do when the rain don't fall?
Sing song kitty catcha kymee-oh
Crops grow small instead of tall
Sing song kitty catcha kymee-oh

Keemo kymo dayro dime
Hey, ho, subble bubble sipso
Periwinkle soapfat, pennywinkle nip cat
Kitty catcha kymee-oh

TIP

70

Change your bottle nipple

There is a science to the design of bottle nipples. They need to allow formula to get through but leave the air behind. Newer bottles are designed with an angle near the nipple end—this makes it more comfortable for you to hold it so that less air gets in with the formula. However, there are also high-tech nipples that actually are antivacuum and can, by themselves, limit the amount of air your baby swallows (Avent bottles, about $4.75 for a four-oz. bottle; 1-800-542-8368). Using these will limit colicky crying, however, only to the degree that swallowed air is *causing* the colicky crying.

TIP

Front carriers

A front carrier ("Snugli") is a soft harness that is worn like a backpack, except that it is worn in front, and the baby is what you pack in it.

The good things about a front carrier are: (1) It provides warmth and close bodily contact for your baby and is one of the most comforting ways to be held during inconsolable crying; (2) It tunes out some of the bright lights, loud noises, and strong smells of the world-at-large; and (3) It frees your arms for other things besides carrying the baby, such as wrangling his older brother into the stroller, talking on the telephone, or nothing at all!

The only drawbacks to putting a screaming baby into a front carrier are: (1) It sometimes takes an engineer to maneuver the various snaps, straps, and holes; and (2) Her vocal cords are just inches from your ears.

TIP

72

SleepTight®

It is possible to simulate the feel of riding in a car (at 55 mph) in the comfort of your baby's own crib. SleepTight® is a device, approved by the FDA, that creates the feeling of a late-night car ride. It is manufactured by Ross Laboratories and is available by calling 1-800-NO-COLIC. It costs $90, which is roughly the equivalent of the gasoline you'll need for YY car trips at ZZ minutes per trip.(You do the math!) If riding in the car truly works for your baby, this may be a worthwhile investment (unless you happen to like late-night driving).

TIP

73

Tummy massage

The proponents of massage therapy for babies stress the invaluable health benefits of massage: improved muscle coordination, skin quality, lung capacity, easing of digestion, and so on. There are certainly some undeniable benefits, but I would scale them down to the more modest claims of enhanced close, physical contact with your baby. Rubbing his belly when he is screaming can be the first step on the road to calming him down. Gas *may* contribute to colic, and this will, in fact, help his tummy feel better.

It is also helpful for tense moms to work off some of the frustration and pent-up energy that comes with having an extremely irritable baby. Do note, though, that the theory that tense parents create colicky babies is 100 percent horsefeathers. My wife and I are two of the mellowest people around, and our babies were colicky for 684 months. Each.

TIP

74

Allover massage

If he likes having his tummy rubbed, massage his feet, his arms and legs, his scalp. Make sure the room is warm, since he needs to be uncovered. You may want to use a gentle lotion or massage oil (just a tiny amount should do), but be on the lookout for rashes that may develop later—a sign of sensitive skin. There are lots of books written that describe specific baby massage techniques, oils, and other pearls of wisdom.

Then, go ahead and give him a relaxing rubdown. If you learn what works during the times that he's relatively calm and peaceful, it will serve as a valuable calming tool when he's crying.

TIP

Song: "Kookaburra"

This is an Australian ditty. Try singing it with an Australian accent. For example, the word "old" can be pronounced "ow-led," and "gay" ought to sound like "guy."

Kookaburra sits in the old gum tree
Merry, merry king of the bush is he
Laugh, Kookaburra! Laugh!
Kookaburra, Gay your life must be

Kookaburra sits in the old gum tree
Eating all the gum drops he can see
Stop, Kookaburra! Stop!
Kookaburra, Leave some there for me

Song: "Lullaby and Good Night" ("Brahms' Lullaby")

(No, I didn't know there were "real" words to this one, either.) The tune is the classic lullaby ("Go to sleep! Go to sleep! Go to sleep my baby!") tune you've known all these years. Turns out we were all wrong about the words.

Lullaby, and good night,
With pink roses bedight,
With lilies o'erspread,
Is my baby's sweet head.
Lay you down now, and rest,
May your slumber be blessed!
Lay you down now, and rest,
May thy slumber be blessed!

Lullaby, and good night,
You're your mother's delight,
Shining angels beside
My darling abide.
Soft and warm is your bed,
Close your eyes and rest
your head.
Soft and warm is your bed,
Close your eyes and rest
your head.
Sleepyhead, close your eyes.
Mother's right here beside you.

I'll protect you from harm,
You will wake in my arms.
Guardian angels are near,
So sleep on, with no fear.
Guardian angels are near,
So sleep on, with no fear.

Lullaby, and sleep tight.
Hush! My darling is
sleeping,
On his sheets white as cream,
With his head full of dreams.
When the sky's bright with
dawn,
He will wake in the morning.
When noontide warms the
world,
He will frolic in the sun.

TIP

Aromatherapy

You interact with your baby by using all of her senses: touch, sight, hearing, and don't forget smell. To your baby, one of the calming things about you is your scent. As with massage, there are those who attribute a variety of near-miraculous healing or anti-infective qualities to various scents. They probably do have soothing properties, and certainly a little air freshening never did anyone any harm (although ingestion of concentrated oils or scented candles *can*).

Used as a candle or lotion, scents such as chamomile, sandalwood, or almond will make you feel a little better about things as well. Eucalyptus is often touted as a cure, or at least an aid, for congestion and wheezing. I do not personally have any strong beliefs for or against aromatherapy from a medical standpoint, so give it a whirl. Your baby might like it.

TIP

78

Six states of baby awareness

A baby has six distinct states of awareness, and recognizing them is one of the first steps to dealing with intertwined sleeping and crying problems. They are:

1. Deep sleep.
2. Active (REM sleep), a lighter stage of sleep. Dreaming, twitching, and facial movements occur in REM sleep.
3. Drowsiness.
4. Awake, alert.
5. Awake, fussy.
6. Crying.

Sleep problems during the first year of life usually occur during *active* sleep and take place at predictable intervals. Inability to get to sleep is a disruption of the *drowsy* period. Babies who are *fussy and awake* are expressing physical needs. They are managed differently than babies in a *crying* state whereby crying serves to shut out the world in order to assimilate the day's events and experiences. Responding to a baby during this phase requires understanding his or her temperament, not just supplying food or a clean diaper.

TIP

The inconsistent baby

An *irregular* baby is one who has difficulty keeping to a schedule or is inconsistent from one day to the next. He does not know if he is unhappy from being hungry, tired, or having a wet diaper. He may become bored easily. What works well to soothe him one day may fail to do so the next. The difference between this kind of behavior and colic is that colic may occur in a baby who is otherwise quite manageable.

There are two ways to approach such a situation: Go with the flow or go against the grain. If you can, compile a mental (or written!) checklist of those things that calm him down and those that don't, and offer the ones that work on an as-needed basis. On the other hand, some irregular babies can be gently coaxed into some semblance of a schedule. If he likes a snack and a nap, make this the basis of a daily routine, and expand it to include a bath, a fuller meal, a longer nap.

TIP

80

The jittery baby

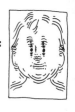

A *jittery* baby is unhappy every time he is faced with something new. He cries when he is handed off to someone else, he cries when he is offered a bottle instead of the breast, or he cries when he hears a loud noise.

Such babies are relatively amenable to a regular schedule. Feed him in the same holding position each day, limit visitors so that he can get used to new faces, and try to keep bath- and naptimes similar from day to day.

With a jittery baby, Dad may not feel like he is part of the picture, as his brand-new son may constantly reject him. This is just a phase and will pass. He will have many opportunities to parent his baby. Of course, the more hands-on dad can be (and not all dads have the luxury to spend this kind of time), the less jittery baby will be with dad.

The high-intensity baby

A *high-intensity* baby may not necessarily be a crier, but if he is—watch out! These babies seem to move more than the typical baby before they are born and are powerful criers when they are hungry, wet, etc.

Like jittery babies, sometimes all that is needed is to turn down the environmental volume. Avoid loud noises and bright lights, and keep older siblings from being in his face when they are home.

On the plus side, these babies can be a ton of fun. Nathan, our second son once used his bouncy seat to propel himself across the floor toward the table, where a bottle awaited. At age three, he is still true to the personality he showed at three months: He now routinely propels himself off higher and higher pieces of furniture, shrieking "Power RAN-gerrrrrrs!" Fortunately, he's indestructible. (We've tested him. He's constructed of a unique rubber-coated titanium-molybdenum alloy.)

TIP

82

The negative baby

A *negative* baby may not be much of a crier. She may, on the other hand, not be much of a smiler or giggler, either. Some babies seem to just have a serious disposition and frown or cry more readily than they smile or laugh.

There's no way to "fix" a negative disposition, but it's not a hard-wired personality trait, either. In time, your baby will learn other ways to express herself, and then the sun will come out from behind the clouds.

TIP

The active baby

An *active* baby is not necessarily a colicky baby. She kicks and grabs at anything she sees or gets distracted easily during feedings. She razzes happily, spraying you in the face constantly. She makes diapering a wrestling match. Like the high-intensity baby, she may have left you with a sore back during pregnancy because of all the kicking.

Here are some tips to calm her down at bedtime or naptime:

- Use books to distract her. Flipping the pages and reading to her should grab her attention.
- Give a long bath.
- Sing soothing songs.
- Talk to her softly.
- Massage her with lotion or oil.
- Swing her in a baby swing.

These babies are quite engaging and can be a lot of fun because they are so responsive. Just make sure to childproof your home early and thoroughly.

TIP

84

The easy baby

For the benefit of you parents who do not have an easy baby, let me reassure you that there is no such thing. The "easy" baby is as mythical as the unicorn, the Loch Ness monster, Bilbo Baggins, the murderer of Vince Foster, or the Perfect Husband.

Those parents who *think* they have the perfect baby have, frankly, a very, very difficult adolescence bearing down on them like a runaway freight train.

TIP

85

Song: "A Welsh Lullaby"

A local au pair we know sings this to her charge. The tune is unrecognizable, and the original title is unpronounceable ("æRoedd Mam yn Cofleidio"), but a rough translation is "A Mother Was Pressing Her Babe."

A mother was pressing her babe to her breast
And saying while soothing his sorrow to rest
Sleep gently my darling, sleep soundly my boy
For thou art my treasure, my rapture and joy
The trumpet is howling again and again
Thy father is sailing a-far on the main
May Heav'n be his shield on the deep heaving sea
And bring him in safely to thee and to me

The lightning was vivid, the thunder was loud
The mother was praying, and sobbing aloud
Amid the wild moaning of nature in strife
The captain sprang forward, and flew to his wife
He kiss'd the fond mother, he kiss'd his dear boy
And gazed on them kindly, exclaiming with joy
"I've made a good fortune, and never will roam
Again from my wife, my sweet child, and my home."

TIP

86

Song: "No, No, Yes, Yes"

The following is not meant to lull a crying baby to sleep. It is supposed to produce a giggle or two, and if you try this out loud right now, I personally guarantee you can't get to the end without laughing yourself. Sung to the tune of "Reveille."

No, no, no, no, no, no, no, no, no, no, no
No, no, no, no, no, no, no, no, no, no, no
No, no, no, no, no, no, no, no, no, no, no
Yes, yes, yes, yes, yes, yes, yes, yes, yes, yes
Yes, yes, yes, yes, yes, yes, yes, yes, yes, yes
Yes, yes, yes, yes, yes, yes, yes, yes, yes, yes

TIP

87

Boxing lessons

Step into the ring. Get your baby in a front carrier, face snuggled into your chest, and go down into the basement and start working out on a punching bag. The baby will respond to both the warm closeness and the rhythm of your motions. You could also probably use the exercise, and it is an early way for dads to start some male bonding with your son.

Equal opportunity alert: Moms, you can do this with your daughters, too. Don't let the guys have all of the fun.

Make eye contact

It hardly seems like a strategy for calming a baby, but babies are more easily soothed with a feeding, singing, diaper change, etc., by a parent who makes significant eye contact during the activity. It teaches her to recognize the person she relies on for her needs and sets the groundwork for that first of developmental milestones, establishing trust. While this may seem to be intuitively obvious, this has been demonstrated scientifically in pediatric behavior research studies. Intuitively, this needs no explanation: it's part of the bond of love.

TIP

89

Take him with you

Through your first few weeks with a new baby, a natural kind of inertia blankets over you. You want to treat your baby delicately, and when he falls asleep, you tiptoe about quietly to avoid waking him. And forget about going anywhere without him—he'll wake up the moment you're out and will wail for you inconsolably.

By the sixth or eighth week, it's time to shake off the sluggishness. If you need to get out of the house, get out and take him with you. Don't plan for a full schedule of shopping and visiting as you might have before his arrival. Instead limit yourself to one or two stops, and allow time to stop and nurse/feed. The lift you get from being in the adult world once more should more than prepare you for the end of baby's day, when he may cry a little longer or louder to react to a world that was slightly more than he was expecting.

TIP

90

Don't force food

*D*on't try to feed a baby who is wailing his head off. This may go against every other commonsense piece of advice you've ever heard; but when a baby is that agitated, he's using every ounce of strength elsewhere: to ball up his arms and legs, eject hurricanes of gas, and shatter your glassware by voice power alone. The *last* thing he's going to be able to do is coordinate sucking and swallowing muscles, cool his respiratory muscles (including the diaphragm—which has been jostling his stomach around so much that he won't feel hungry), and relax enough to allow the milk to stay down. Anything you feed him at that stage could end up in projectile vomiting. Try something else to calm him first, and *then* go for the food.

I hope you're reading this *before* you've gotten into this situation. A half-crazed mom reading this for the first time will, no doubt, promptly send this book into orbit.

Formula with iron

*D*on't take your baby off regular iron-fortified formula if she's not having a bowel movement every day. Babies cry and strain and grunt and then pop out a few tiny pebbles, then offer a winning smile as if to say "My job's all done!" Moms and dads then cry and run to their doctor to get the "okay" for low-iron formula.

There is no basis for this. It is true that nine out of ten mothers will tell you that iron constipates their babies, but it is also true that babies frequently become anemic in the first six months of life. And the only way to assure adequate iron, which optimizes growth and development, is to give it with the formula. The AAP's position is straight-forward: non-breastfed babies should receive high-iron formula. Some doctors may recommend iron in vitamins for babies who are on low-iron formula, but this is not a good solution since the iron in formula is absorbed by the baby's intestinal tract much better than the iron in vitamin drops.

Song: "There Was an Old Woman Who Swallowed a Fly"

This song is really a game, of course, and each verse builds on the last, so I've skipped the ones in the middle. But you get the idea.

There was an old woman who swallowed a fly
I don't know why she swallowed a fly—
Perhaps she'll die!

There was an old woman who swallowed a cow
I don't know how she swallowed a cow.
She swallowed the cow to catch the dog
Oh, what a hog to swallow a dog!...
She swallowed the dog to catch the cat
Imagine that! She swallowed a cat....
She swallowed the cat to catch the bird
How absurd to swallow a bird...
She swallowed the bird to catch the spider
That wiggled and wriggled and jiggled inside her...
She swallowed the spider to catch the fly,
I don't know why she swallowed a fly—
Perhaps she'll die!

There was an old woman who swallowed a horse
She died, of course!

TIP

93

Song: "Waltzing Matilda"

There's nothing like a good Australian song, is there?

Once a jolly swagman, camped by a billabong,
Under the shade of a coolibah tree,
And he sang as he watched
and waited 'til his billy boiled
"You'll come a-waltzing, Matilda, with me"
Waltzing Matilda, Waltzing Matilda
You'll come a-waltzing, Matilda, with me

Down came a jumbuck to drink at the billabong,
Up jumped the swagman
and grabbed him with glee,
And he sang as he stowed
that jumbuck in his tucker bag,
"You'll come a-waltzing, Matilda, with me"

Up jumped the swagman, sprang into the billabong,
"You'll never catch me alive," said he,
And his ghost may be heard
as you pass by the billabong,
You'll come a-waltzing, Matilda, with me.

TIP

94

Bunkmates

Bringing baby to bed, especially to nurse, is a quick way to resolve middle-of-the-night crying, especially in the first month of life. The unintended consequence, however, is that she will quickly become accustomed to sleeping there with you. It is, at best, a truce. Any movement on your or your husband's part may wake her. Even if she's in a bassinet, the sound of snoring can wake her. She will also learn that when she stirs in the middle of the night you *will* feed or comfort her—and won't see any reason why this should not happen every night.

Don't create sleeping problems. Banish her from your bedroom as soon as she reaches the point where she *can* sleep through the night. Tuck the bassinet away and unwrap the crib. Let her sleep in her own room. You will need a one-way monitor so you can hear her when she does cry. And do it soon: It gets harder and harder for an older baby to sleep in a crib all by herself if she's used to sleeping between mom and dad.

TIP

The early riser

When a baby gets up first thing in the morning, she's hungry and her butt is likely to be cold and damp. Wouldn't you cry, too? You will, of course, attend to those basic needs when you get out of bed. But if it's 5:15 A.M., wouldn't you really rather stay in bed?

Some parents, early risers themselves no doubt, may feel that this represents a full night's sleep. The rest of you understand the truth of the situation: The night is far from over. Don't worry. Your baby is malleable. There are ways to trick her into sleeping later in the morning:

- Keep shades and windows closed to shut out early morning light and traffic noise.
- Don't feed her right away. This sets her stomach-clock to go off at 5:15 A.M.
- Put her down later at night, and try to limit daytime naps. She needs about fourteen hours of sleep a day, and you can prod her to take a big chunk of them at night.
- Equip the crib with toys, rattles, and books. If she has something to look at, she'll be happy.

TIP

96

A new mattress

The first few nights of sleeping alone in a crib are often marked by middle-of-the-night crying. Babies are smart; they recognize transitions and breaks from routine and often don't care for the change.

An easily remedied problem may be the crib mattress itself. If you have inherited the family heirloom crib (the mattress grandpa slept on during the Depression), buy a new mattress. A baby needs a firm mattress with no lumps, bumps, or funny smells. Get a mattress pad while you're at it. It's easier to get nasty pee or poo smell out of a mattress *pad* than a whole mattress. Graduation from a bassinet to the crib (and their own bedroom) may take place any time from two to five months, depending on your and your spouse's tolerance for company.

TIP

97

Turn off the noise

*D*on't expose your baby's ears to prolonged bouts of extreme noise. Ninety decibels is loud: a basketball game, a rock concert, a nearby siren. Momentary exposures won't hurt her, but longer exposures may permanently affect hearing and speech development. In short, don't bother taking your baby to the opening of *Jurassic Park III: Even More Dinosaurs* or to watch the Bulls vs. the Knicks. It may seem as if you are going to be confined to your home for the rest of your life, but everything that you used to like to do BC (before children) will still be there when you are finally ready to leave baby in the hands of a baby-sitter (with your pager on, your lists of neighbors' and grandparents' phone numbers, a cell phone, and repeated assurances to your spouse that "she'll be okay").

TIP

98

Chest rub

Lay your hands flat on his chest and gently flutter your fingers over his ribs, establishing a delicate rhythm. As you do this, his crying should start falling into a regular pattern that is in tune with your massaging. You can also try lightly kneading his chest and making circular motions on his tummy.

Once he begins to respond to your touch, he may continue crying, but with less urgency. Don't switch gears and get the bottle (or breast) out. Keep going, because this is a sign that he appreciates what you are doing. Move on to his back, his arms, legs, fingers, and toes (scalp, too!).

The only time to stop this in favor of some other approach is if his crying increases and he seems to be hungry or in need of a diaper change.

TIP

Song: Irish Lullaby ("Too-Ra-Loo-Ra-Loo")

From the au pair network again comes an Irish song to calm the keening wee ones. The way she sings it, I am reminded of an old Van Morrison song, "Waiting for the Sun to Shine," from *Moondance*. Ah, *Moondance*.

Over in Killarney,
Many years ago,
Me mither sang a song to me
In tones so sweet and low.

Just a simple little ditty,
In her good ould Irish way,
And I'd give the world if she could sing
That song to me this day.

Too-ra-loo-ra-loo-ral,
Too-ra-loo-ra-li,
Too-ra-loo-ra-loo-ral,
Hush, now don't you cry!

TIP

100

Too-ra-loo-ra-loo-ral,
Too-ra-loo-ra-li,
Too-ra-loo-ra-loo-ral,
That's an Irish lullaby.

Song: "Little Bunny Foo Foo"

This song requires only a few hand gestures to enhance its general entertainment value.

Little Bunny Foo Foo, hopping through the forest (hold fore and middle fingers out like rabbit ears)

Scooping up the field mice and boppin' 'em on the head (bop baby on head with rabbit-ear fingers)

Down came the good fairy and she said (point at baby)

"Little Bunny Foo Foo, I don't want to see you (shake finger, as if reprimanding, switch voices)

Scooping up the field mice and boppin' 'em on the head. (bop baby again— gently of course)

I'll give you three chances, and if you don't behave I'll turn you into a goon!"

The next day:

Little Bunny Foo Foo, hopping through the forest...

I'll give you two more chances, and if you don't behave I'll turn you into a goon!"

The next day:
Same but one more chance

The next day:

Little Bunny Foo Foo, I don't like your attitude.

Scooping up the field mice . . .

I gave you three chances and you didn't behave

Now you're a goon! POOF!!"

The moral of the story is: HARE TODAY, GOON TOMORROW

TIP

101

Nature's Cradle®

This is high-tech stuff. The Nature's Cradle® infant mattress system, according to the manufacturer, "simulates Mom's gentle walking motion and internal rhythms of the third trimester." A gently rocking mattress is accompanied by soft amniotic fluid sounds and the comforting rhythm of a heartbeat. Even more ingeniously, the motion and sound diminish slowly over the first four months, gradually weaning your baby off them. After that, you've got a plain vanilla mattress. This company also makes a bassinet. Both are available at some baby-product retail stores or by phone at (800) 900-9480.

All this doesn't come cheap. The list price is $399. The product is not guaranteed, but the manufacturer, Infant Advantage Inc., claims that it reduces crying by 65 percent. The company's Web page is filled with lots of ecstatic reviews from newspapers, magazines, and morning TV shows.

TIP

102

Rotate diapering

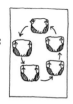

D on't be the only one to do the diapering, and don't accept shoddy work.

If there is a husband in America left who claims he is incapable of changing a diaper, then sign him up for Medicare and get him a "handicapped" license plate. Diapering is not rocket science, and it *is* a chance for some special bonding.

Be attentive, however. If your baby develops rashes frequently when someone else is diapering her, they may not be cleaning her bottom thoroughly, or they may not be consistently using occlusive (i.e., zinc oxide) creams, most of which can be applied with every change. Rashes are almost always preventable with good hygiene.

TIP

103

Belly raspberries

Just think—if a belly raspberry is half as delicious for baby as it is for you, then you're at least twice the parent you think you are!

There are some times that are better for razzing than others. At the start of a diaper change, for example, a good snarf on the belly button makes him much happier and more cooperative—if you can stand the smell, that is. Also, as you're getting him undressed for a bath, he may get fussy and uncooperative. This, too, is a good time to get physical with him.

Don't try to perturb his tummy too much after a meal or if he's cranky and winding down to go to bed. This is something many dads are tempted to do.

And if he really likes his razzes, try it under the arms or on the thighs.

TIP

104

Snuggle game:
Leg, foot, toe toe toe

This is a snuggle game that teaches body parts.

Start with baby sitting in your lap, and point his hand to his nose and then yours, saying "Nose!" in a deep voice each time. Go back and forth once or twice. Then do the same for chin, mouth, teeth, and eyes.

Then move to chest and belly. When you get to the arm, go "Arm, hand, thumb, finger, finger, finger, finger!" tracing your finger down his arm to his hand and each finger. Do each arm.

When you get to the legs, say "Leg, foot, toe, toe, toe, toe, toe," ending up with a tickle to the bottom of the feet.

Most babies will let you do this roughly two or three dozen times before they get tired of it and want to do something else.

TIP

Snuggle game: Where is thumbkin?

This is sung to the tune of "Frere Jacques":
(Start with your hand behind your back)

Where is thumbkin? Where is thumbkin?
(bring left fist forward, thumb up)
Here I am! Here I am! (bring right fist out, thumb up)
How are you this morning? (left thumb "talks"
to right)
Very well I thank you (right thumb "answers")
Run away! (hide left hand) *Run away!* (hide
right hand)

The next verses are:

Where is pointer? Where is pointer?
(second finger) …
Where is middie? Where is middie? (third finger) …
Where is ringo? Where is ringo? (fourth finger)…
Where is pinky? Where is pinky? (pinky)…
Where is the family? Where is the family? (wave
the whole hand)…

Snuggle game: This little piggy

Everybody knows "This little piggy went to market." But if your baby is crying unhappily, the familiar old games like this sometimes just don't cut it. Start out by cuddling him in your lap, warm his feet up in your hands (if they're cold), and play "This little piggy" just to let him know what you're up to. Then when you get to the other foot, start out something like this:

This little dinosaur went to the swamp
   (wiggle the pinky toe)
This little dinosaur rolled in the mud
   (wiggle the fourth toe)
This little dinosaur ate hamburgers
   (wiggle the third toe)
And this little dinosaur had to burp!
   (wiggle the first toe)
Oops! I missed this dinosaur and he ran away
   (run fingers up to tummy/neck)

TIP

107

Milk allergy

An allergy to cow's milk may cause crying directly following a feeding. Vomiting, excessive spitting up after feeding, and/or loose stools are also often present. Breastfeeding mothers who consume lots of dairy products may pass the cow's milk protein along to their infant and cause symptoms of allergy in protein-sensitive infants. Elimination of all dairy and beef products from mom's diet for ten days may improve the situation.

A true milk allergy is actually quite uncommon. More often, the problem is technically a lactose intolerance, the inability to digest the lactose sugar present in milk. An infant who is formula fed and has a true milk allergy should receive a soy-based formula, if tolerated, but often needs a truly hypoallergenic formula, such as Pregestimil or Nutramigen.

TIP

Stuffy nose

Young babies always seem to have congested noses. (A runny nose is a distinctly different problem.) Most of these babies do not have a viral infection. Stuffiness may not bother them; however, when the condition interferes with eating or is so bad that it causes irritability, there are a number of things to do:

- Saline nose drops, such as Ocean drops or NaSal, can help clear your baby's nose. You can also make them yourself. Add a quarter teaspoon of salt to four ounces of water and drip it in with a dropper.
- Use a cold-air humidifier in cooler weather or if the air in your home is dry.
- Turn the water on in the shower all the way to hot and let the room fill with mist, then sit there with baby for fifteen to twenty minutes.
- Suction the nose with a nasal aspirator after trying any of these methods.

TIP

Don't sweat a runny nose

Over-the-counter cold preparations can actually make fussy babies with colds cry *more*. Since they promote drying of secretions in the upper respiratory passages (nose and throat), they may make feeding more difficult and may make it hard for your baby to breathe because of thick, tenacious mucus stuck in the baby's nose. Mother Nature knows what she is doing. The chances are that your baby's runny nose bothers *him* a whole lot less than it does you. If you can stand the sight of it, let it run. Stay away from medications that may—at best—marginally improve a runny nose for a day or two and are more likely to cause a fight to get him to take it.

TIP

110

Pacifiers

Using a pacifier to *head off* a steamroller of a cry is the easiest and potentially most helpful thing you can do for your baby—and for your nerves. A pacifier helps your baby focus on an activity he likes and helps tune out some of the stimuli of an overly loud or busy environment. Pacifiers were generally held in low regard by the last generation of parents, and there will be more than a few new grandparents recoiling in horror as you stick one in their grandchild's mouth. At this age, it does *not* ruin their teeth, it does *not* spoil them, and they do *not* become dependent on it. The only thing you need to be aware of is when to stop giving a pacifier—it comes sooner than you might think.

A caveat: Just make sure your baby isn't hungry. (If he is, the pacifier won't work for long anyway.)

TIP

Another great reflex

Assuming you don't have anything
contagious, blow directly but gently onto
the baby's forehead. She immediately will blink
her eyes and take a deep breath. I have seen this
reflex persist for as long as six months in some
babies. Repeat this once or twice, and she may
forget what she was crying about in the first
place. This also works best once the baby is
already calming down, but it may help get
things moving in the right direction.

TIP

112

Jiggled, not stirred

A dad I know discovered this colic cure for crying by accident. He had a nervous habit of restlessly jiggling his leg no matter what he was doing: watching basketball on TV, talking on the phone, anything and everything. The leg was always in motion. When his first colicky baby came along, he would place her face down on her belly on his lap and gently pat her back. And he would, without knowing it, jiggle her up and down with his ever-active leg. Once he realized this, he tried it *without* the patting, and it seemed just as effective. It became her and his favorite anti-colic position.

One big, big caveat: Jiggling is not tossing or shaking. A baby should never become airborne, and his head shouldn't bounce. And if your baby is at all unhappy with just jiggling, don't do it. If you don't know if you feel safe doing this, call your doctor to have her watch you do it.

TIP

113

Just say no: Roughhousing

It's a law of nature that dads play rougher with babies than moms and are more physical when trying to calm them. A common paternal inclination is to try and soothe baby by tossing him in the air. *Never* do this with a young baby. Even gently letting a baby become airborne can cause unintentional injuries to the head, neck, or eyes. Similar caution must be exercised against swinging the baby around in a circle too quickly, which can also cause injuries from sudden deceleration or inadvertent impact. You will have lots of years ahead of you in which to play airplane, helicopter, pull-my-finger, etc., but the time for that is definitely not now.

TIP

114

Switch detergents

Babies have sensitive skin. A baby who is constantly cranky and fussy may be bothered by the feel of his clothes against his skin. You may have tried changing his formula, the carrying position, his pacifier; now it may be time to try changing his detergent. This will subtly change the texture or scent, and he may be less sensitive to the chemicals in the new soap.

Some clues to the possibility that your detergent is a culprit for crying:

- He only seems happy wearing new outfits.
- Skin rashes persist, particularly in creases where clothes are in close contact with the skin.
- Strong family history of eczema or environmental allergies.

Cold care

The cranky, fatigued, whimpery cry of a baby who is sick with a cold is difficult for any parent. It's usually crystal clear that she wants nothing more than to be held all day long—and even then she whimpers. Some things to keep in mind until she does feel better:

- *Let* her rest in your arms all day long.
- Let her nap as much as she needs.
- She needs all the calories she can get. She may not have any appetite at all for solids but may take bottle after bottle. If she drinks formula but can't tolerate it, give her a balanced hydration solution (Pedialyte, Ricelyte, Rehydralyte), and she'll need nothing more (even very sick babies can usually continue to take breastmilk). You can give a re-hydration solution for one or two days, by which time her appetite should return anyway. If she prefers the taste of soup, a clear, low-sodium broth is fine if baby is over nine months old.
- If your baby refuses even liquids, you need to watch for signs of dehydration: no tears when she cries, dry diapers for more than six to eight hours, or stringy saliva in the mouth. If any of these signs appear, call your doctor.

TIP

Try a parenting course

If you've lost the manual that came with your baby, sign up for a parenting course, where they will hand you a new one. Such courses can serve as a reliable introduction to your baby's needs, capabilities, and typical problems. They are often taught by nurses, doctors, or other professionals experienced in caring for children and who are likely to be more authoritative than your friends' well-meaning advice. Check with the hospital where you delivered, your ob/gyn, pediatrician, or family practitioner for upcoming courses. You can also network with other new moms (and dads) and see what *they* do for crying babies.

Most worthwhile courses will give you a recommended reading list, but until you get there, I recommend *What to Expect the First Year* by Arlene Eisenberg. It is a comprehensive approach to caring for infants and is well organized. The challenges and delights of babies are presented in a month-by-month format, along with a host of other informative sections.

TIP

117

Call your mother

A grandmother can be a wonderful thing to have, if you're a newborn. And handing a crying baby off to grandma or grandpa can be a tremendous source of relief for mom and dad. Grandma may know a thing or two about rocking and comforting, and there are few people you can trust with your baby as completely as your own mother or mother-in-law. However, there are some important issues to consider:

- She raised you (or your husband) a lot differently. Things have changed since then, so a little flexibility is important for both of you. Be prepared to listen to her, and make sure she is prepared to listen to you.
- Try to put aside whatever "mother-in-law" issues may have existed in the past, and keep in mind that, if she is available and willing to help, now she is primarily "grandma."
- She may have some dough stashed away. Play your cards right and that college education you've been so worried about is a done deal.

TIP

118

Teaching others about your infant

If you return to work while your baby is still colicky, it will be important to let the baby's primary caregiver know what works best to calm him. Try to let the caregiver know when your baby usually gets hungry, when naptimes are, and what you do when your baby is crying just for the sake of crying. If you have established a ritual of diaper changing while singing a particular song, give a full demonstration (hopefully a successful one), and then watch your baby's caregiver do it. You can see how baby reacts to a new person and may be able to come up with a new strategy if needed.

The foregoing applies to grandma as well. Her good intentions and 20+ year-old habits should take a back seat to what you *know* works for your baby.

TIP

119

The long-distance rescue

You're back at work at last, having some adult conversation, listening to everyone "ooh" and "aah" over your baby pictures, and feeling that your first few weeks have been successful. Then, of course, the call comes: He's been crying for an hour and nothing seems to work.

Assuming for the moment that your baby's caregiver has fed him, changed him, and tried to get him to go down for a nap, *and* also assuming that going home is only a last resort, try long-distance parenting. Sing him his favorite song over the telephone and mix it in with a little gentle cooing. It may take a few minutes to get him to begin winding down.

You *know* your baby's cry. If it's a regular fussy cry, it's a good bet that if you throw in the towel and run back to baby, he will be peaceful or sleeping. If you think baby may be sick or in real pain, you or your spouse *will* probably need to check on him in person.

TIP

120

Be prepared!

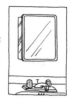

Before a crisis occurs, it is helpful to prepare a few things ahead of time.

Have a first aid kit ready, and take a training course (or refresher course if it's been a long time since you first trained) in infant CPR. Check to make sure that 911 is the number to call in your community in case of emergencies. Most but not all areas have a standing EMS (Emergency Medical Services) system.

Check with your doctor about which hospital he will send you to if you have to go to the ER; it may not be the same one you delivered in. If time permits, call your managed care plan to preauthorize the visit, or ask that your doctor do this if he tells you to go to the ER. Make sure you have enough cash with you for whatever needs may arise because you may be stuck there for hours. If you have to bring other children along, they will get bored and cranky, so you might want to grab a few toys if time permits.

Finally, bring along your baby's immunization and health record and all medications he is on, if any. If there is a suspected poisoning, bring along the bottle of pills or liquid ingested. Keeping a cool head is a very quick way of gaining the trust and respect of your sick child and the treating hospital personnel.

TIP

Fever, part 1

Fever is not an illness, it is a symptom of illness. A fever with any kind of infection is enough to make your baby cranky, inconsolable, and sometimes sleepy. Particularly under the age of three months, it is important to notify your doctor if your baby develops a fever, and he or she can assess the situation. In some cases, tests are appropriate to see if there is a bacterial or urinary infection present, which requires antibiotics. Viral infections will usually go away by themselves without antibiotics.

In most cases, a doctor will be able to reassure you that all is well. Acetaminophen (Tylenol) in the infant suspension (80 mg/ml) may be given and lowers the fever by 1–3 degrees F for a few hours. (Note: Most infant acetaminophen bottles come with a dropper marked in 0.4 ml increments.) Ibuprofen (Motrin) is also a good fever killer for infants six months or older.

Medication	Dose	Amount	Frequency
Acetaminophen	5–7 mg/pound	80 mg/ml	every 4 hours
Ibuprofen	3.5–5 mg/pound	20 mg/ml	every 6–8 hours

TIP

Discovering an incarcerated hernia

A hernia is a hole in a muscle wall. In baby boys, a hernia in the lower abdominal wall may let a loop of intestine slide into the scrotum which can become trapped, swollen, and be unable to slide back into the abdominal cavity. This is a serious condition, but it can be readily diagnosed and treated. Your doctor will recommend taking your baby to the ER, where your baby will be sedated and an attempt made to push the incarcerated intestine back through the hernia into the abdomen where it belongs. Once this is done, a simple uncomplicated operation can be arranged at a later date to close the hole in the muscle.

Both the sudden crying this condition produces and the corresponding bulge in the scrotum are obvious. A word of advice: Don't stick around to watch the actual procedure.

The same situation may also occur in girls, but this is rare. One of the labia will appear bulging and red, and the sudden crying is the same as in boys.

TIP

Just say no: broccoli

A popular notion, never proven nor disproven, is that broccoli or other elements in the nursing mother's diet, such as garlic, cauliflower, cabbage, onions, and turnips, cause gas, and hence colic, in a breastfed infant. Eliminating broccoli from your diet is probably not a difficult way to minimize your baby's intestinal sensitivity. It may take a few days to tell if it helps. If it doesn't work, you might try cutting some of the other offenders from your diet. If you end up on an ascetic regime of rice and water and the baby is still crying, go back to your normal (sensible) diet and look for other ways to help your baby.

TIP

124

Reflux

Gastroesophageal reflux is the term given to the spitting up that most babies will have in their first few months of life (Dave Barry discovered—and I swear I am not making this up— this is anatomically caused by "the returning food loop"). In a small number of babies, reflux causes pain from the irritating effects of stomach acids on the esophagus. When babies become irritable and uncomfortable from reflux, there are a couple of worthwhile things that can be done before turning to the doctor for medication:

- Elevate the head of the bed by about 10–15° by placing a pillow under the mattress. Place a blanket roll under the baby's tush and along her sides to keep her from sliding downward or along the sides of the crib.
- Thicken her formula or expressed milk with a small amount of rice cereal, usually a teaspoon or two for each four ounces.

TIP

Gastroenteritis

Gastroenteritis, or stomach flu, is rare under three months of age, particularly in breastfed infants (breast milk provides unsurpassed immunity against intestinal infection). Vomiting, fever, and diarrhea are often signs of a mild, viral intestinal infection. The vomiting may come first and is usually of brief duration, but all three symptoms may arrive together. In an uncomplicated course, dehydration does not occur, and it often resolves itself in three to four days. It is best to stay away from cow's milk or other dairy products at this time (breast milk is tolerated better).You should offer your baby a nutritionally balanced, clear liquid formula such as Ricelyte, Pedialyte, or Rehydralyte. When you resume formula, start with a half-strength dilution, followed by full strength if the diluted stuff is tolerated. As always, call your doctor if you aren't sure about things.

Don't even think about it: Herb teas

Herb teas are for *you*. *Don't* offer them to your baby, despite what an herbalist may tell you. In fact, herbal teas may contain caffeine or other active ingredients that are innocuous for adults but could have toxic effects in babies. If you are breastfeeding, a small amount (one cup a day) for mom is probably fine. More than that should be avoided, since caffeine may pass into breast milk. Be wary of poorly (or un-) labeled substances, as these may contain chemicals that are undesirable for babies. Any legitimate herbal tea or other "natural" substance should follow proper FDA labeling guidelines since they are regulated as dietary products. Then, if you still do not have a good idea of what you are dealing with, you can call the company. Many indicate on the label how to contact them for questions—and they do like to tell you about their products.

TIP

Anal fissures

A hard bowel movement may produce an anal fissure—a thin, superficial skin tear along the anus. Crying is typically worst during bowel movements, and there is often red, "fresh" blood mixed in with the stool (unlike internal bleeding, which looks black or tarry). The appearance of bright red blood in small amounts in the diaper is almost always a result of a minor tear in a capillary, which looks like a much more worrisome condition than it really is. Such fissures heal quickly, within a day or two, often unaided or with the application of a small amount of antibiotic ointment at each diaper change. If the amount of blood increases or it persists for more than about three stools, call your doctor.

After a DPT shot

Fussiness in the forty-eight hours following a DPT vaccine is common. There is often a fever and redness at the site of injection, each of which is more exaggerated with subsequent shots. After the first or second vaccine, fever may not be prominent; however, Tylenol or Motrin in appropriate doses may help lessen baby's fussiness. If the baby responds to this, you probably do not need to call your doctor, but you should let him/her know about this reaction at the next visit. If the crying is high-pitched or the baby is inconsolable, call your doctor.

The reaction is usually due to the "P," or pertussis, portion of the vaccine, which, until 1997, had been composed of the *entire* pertussis bacteria. In February 1997, the FDA licensed an "acellular" pertussis vaccine, composed of only a few pertussis proteins. These proteins provide all the protection of the original vaccine but, in trials conducted by the NIH over a period of years, have far fewer side effects. As a result, the new "DTaP" vaccine is becoming the routine vaccine given to all babies and should take some of the sting out of a necessary but unpleasant side of babyhood.

TIP

Don't even think about it: Alcohol

A lcohol is a potentially lethal toxin. It causes severe hypoglycemia in babies, which may cause seizures or brain damage. *Don't* ever give alcohol to a baby. Despite what grandpa or an overly cavalier uncle urges ("Give him a sip! It'll calm him right down."), they're wrong. Keep the liquor away from all other children in the house as well to keep *them* safe and to avoid the potential of them giving it to the baby. To further safeguard against this, never pour alcohol out of its original container into another one that might be mistaken for a safe drink.

TIP

130

Corneal abrasion

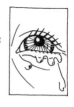

Babies scratch themselves. Their arms are usually flexed at the elbow, placing their fingers up around the face. As they reflexively open and close their fists, they sometimes leave small, superficial facial scratches. On rare instances they may inadvertently poke themselves in the eye and scratch the cornea. The cornea is the clear lens covering the pupil and is exquisitely sensitive to touch, and it is often the largest exposed part of the eye. The crying produced by a corneal abrasion is dramatic, sharp, and painful. The other signs of a corneal abrasion are subtle—a pink eye or excess squinting. The change in the quality of the cry is often the best indicator.

Here's the good news: An astute doctor often considers the possibility of a corneal scratch when presented with a suddenly "colicky" baby. It is easily diagnosed by placing a fluorescent dye onto the eye. A scratch heals itself without treatment, often in only a day. Adults with a corneal abrasion are often given an eyepatch and narcotics to relieve the pain. Acetaminophen alone is appropriate pain medication for babies with a scratch, and the patch is not usually needed.

TIP

Hair tourniquet

Here's another oddball that is an occasional cause for crying: A long strand of hair (mother's, father's, or baby's) may wrap itself around a finger, toe, or the penis. It acts like a tourniquet and cuts off circulation. When this happens, the first thing that you will notice is crying, often an abrupt, painful cry much like the crying present with a corneal abrasion. When you look closely at the baby, a hair tourniquet is obvious: a purple fingertip or toe tip (I have never seen one wrapped around the penis, nor do I ever want to) and a thin cutoff line of the coiled hair.

Call the doctor. He/she may be able to remove the hair with tweezers, but an ER referral is often appropriate, since a magnifying-glass headset (the dweeby things you sometimes see in old TV doctor shows) is needed to see that all the loops have been removed—there are often several—and to decide whether there is a need for antibiotics.

TIP

132

Birth injury symptoms

Injuries are rare in the first three months of life. Babies are swaddled, blanketed, and treated very, very delicately, even by rank amateurs like disgruntled older siblings and your still-single friends. An accident that causes bruising (over a joint such as the elbow or shoulder, or even a head bonk) is almost always trivial and, unlike us grown-ups, rarely causes pain or persistent crying.

The most significant injuries at this age are birth injuries. They include clavicle fractures, which are surprisingly pain-free, unless the area is accidentally touched. They heal within a few weeks. A lump over the break is often noted sometime after the fact.

Other birth injuries involve twisting the shoulder and stretching the arm's nerves, and these, too, are often painless. The limp arm is held at the side, and a sling is all that is needed until the nerves recover function, usually over a period of ten to twenty days.

TIP

133

Thrush

Thrush is a yeast infection of the moist surfaces inside the mouth. Small, white plaques appear, which look just like a coating of milk on the tongue, gums, or inside of the cheeks. The plaques firmly adhere to these surfaces and may bleed slightly if rubbed off, which makes for an uncomfortable feeding experience for your baby. Thrush is often accompanied by a yeast infection in the diaper area or a maternal yeast infection. It crops up most commonly in the first eight to twelve weeks of life, but may appear after a course of antibiotics (for, say, an ear infection) any time thereafter. It is easily treated by an oral antifungal solution, which can be prescribed by your baby's doctor (and get some for yourself if you need to at the same time). Apply a small amount to a cotton swab and roll it over the affected areas three or four times a day. This ought to take care of it in just a few days.

TIP

134

Eczema

Eczema is a chronic skin condition characterized by patches of excess flaking, oozing, and hyperreactivity. In severe cases, the areas affected can be quite extensive. The onset may be in early infancy, particularly when there is a history of asthma, environmental allergies, or eczema among other family members. Eczematous skin may be quite irritated, raw, and painful to your baby. For mild cases, avoidance of certain detergents or synthetic fabrics may be helpful (except cotton, which is rarely a culprit), as is use of moisturizing lotion. Steroid creams are available in 0.5 or 1 percent strengths without a prescription; however, it is advisable to check with your doctor before using one.

TIP

Don't even think about it: Adult medication

There are no drugs that cure colic or reliably stop crying, or, aside from the *very* questionable benefit of simethicone in some babies, even make a bit of difference. *Don't* give any medications to calm him down; and if you suspect pain or some medical condition, don't do a thing before you check with your doctor. If there is a toddler about the house, make sure he or she knows *never* to give baby medicine, and always keep drugs locked up and away from children, even (especially) nonprescription medications, which are okay for adults and adults only. They all contain active ingredients that may have harmful effects in babies.

TIP

136

Keep a record

You certainly don't need one *more* thing to do, but if you are truly at your wit's end about what is and is not working for your baby, keep a written record to guide your future efforts. Some important items that belong in a "crying diary" are:

- What time did an individual crying episode begin?
- What were the circumstances (i.e., just fed, woke up screaming, loud noises)?
- What methods did you try?
- Did anything work?
- How long did the crying last?
- What stopped it?

Over the course of a week, a pattern may emerge that may not have been otherwise apparent to you—a pattern that may allow you to change the way you respond or the way you organize your baby's day to avoid certain stresses or situations that appear to upset him.

TIP

Feeling guilty

Sometimes, in the crazed rush of a new life with a constantly crying baby, there are times when you feel like your common sense just isn't working any more. After all, if it were working, then after feeding, burping, changing, bathing, jiggling, feeding *again*, changing *again*, and cooing to your baby *again*, somewhere along the line your baby would have contentedly drifted off to sleep, or at least settled down for a few minutes. And yet, there she is, all thirteen pounds of her, endlessly crying away. No wonder you want to know when *your* needs are going to be met.

Don't feel guilty about having these thoughts. Every good parent has also, at one time or another, felt like they could not take another second of parenting. This is normal. Talk your feelings over with your spouse, who has also probably felt the same way and may feel guilty about mentioning it to you—and that would probably do you both good. Just, um, *don't* mention it to the grandparents.

TIP

138

The hand-off

Always try to have a backup person to whom you can hand the baby when her crying gets to be too much. Every so often you need to get her off your hands and take a rest from the (wrongly) guilty feelings of "What am I doing wrong?" or "What am I forgetting to do?" that come from seeing your little loved one so unhappy. (Your ears could also use the rest!) You may also want to tend to other responsibilities, including other children. If they're old enough, let one of them take baby. Relax and recharge your batteries for the next round of battle.

If you are a single parent and you *know* you're in for a bout of colic later on in the day, arrange for a friend or relative to be available even for a little while. Just knowing that you have support can make the crying that much more bearable.

TIP

Go public

If you need to breastfeed and you are in a public place, by all means feed your baby. His needs come before the objections of any observers who may think otherwise. Never keep your baby crying until you can find a public bathroom, and never, never accept the disapproval of others as a reason to shortchange you and your baby. You should never forget the enormous advantages of nursing and that you chose to do it for very good reasons.

According to one survey reported in *Child* magazine, about one-quarter of all breastfeeding women have experienced negative reactions or comments from bystanders, but an equal amount have received positive, encouraging remarks. Discretion during nursing is certainly called for, though, so be prepared and bring along a scarf or other wrap. With older babies, this will also serve the dual purpose of minimizing distractions while they nurse. If you have an older sibling along, pack an activity for them to allow you to nurse in peace.

TIP

140

Positive reinforcement

When your baby finally manages to do something that helps him calm himself down, like putting his fist or thumb in his mouth, be sure to reinforce it with a lot of happy, excited chatter and cooing. Do not, for a moment, ever underestimate the power of being your baby's parent. Even at his worst moments, he will be happy to hear your voice. It's still the thing in the world that means the most to him, and he probably can distinguish between a happy, excited parent and an annoyed, irritated one.

Moms are far more likely to experience this sooner than dads. They are more often the primary caregiver and may pick up on the subtleties sooner as well.

Don't worry, dad. Your time will come when you can be your son's hero just by sinking a free throw, playing a wicked air guitar, giving him money, or popping in a video.

TIP

Song: "Five Little Monkeys"

Sometimes a song helps heal a boo-boo. If
your little monkey just fell, try this:

Five little monkeys jumping on the bed
One fell off and bumped his head
So Momma called the doctor and the doctor said
No more monkeys jumping on the bed!

Four little monkeys jumping on the bed
One fell off and bumped his head
So Momma called the doctor and the doctor said
No more monkeys jumping on the bed!

Three little monkeys jumping on the bed
One fell off and bumped his head
So Momma called the doctor and the doctor said
No more monkeys jumping on the bed!

Then, two little monkeys jumping on the bed;

Then, one little monkey jumping on the bed

Then, no little monkeys jumping on the bed
None fell off and bumped his head
So Momma called the doctor and the doctor said
Put those monkeys back in bed!

TIP

142

3-12 MONTHS:
BABYHOOD

Bubbles

Under the same assumption that anything that distracts a baby's attention while he's crying is good, try a bottle of bubbles. That's right, the play soap bubbles with the wand inside. These are a perennially popular toy for older children, but older babies will be fascinated by the way they float randomly through the air, as well as the improbable swirl of light playing across their surface. And watch for the look of surprise on their face when the bubbles pop.

Just try to avoid letting the bubbles burst directly over the face. The soap will get in their eyes, and then you will be in for some big-league crying.

TIP

Car keys

A rattle by any other shape is still a rattle. Once your baby has mastered a little eye-hand control, give him a ring of keys and let him entertain himself. If he becomes interested enough to stop crying, he will, no doubt, begin to explore it by slapping the keys against a tabletop, tasting the keys, and throwing them. He could, conceivably, poke himself in the eye, but this must be a rare occurrence, as I have never treated this kind of injury in the ER nor have I heard of anyone who has.

I suppose we ought to give babies credit where credit is due.

Another Stroller Technique

In time, you will become a stroller artist. When wildly racing to and fro in the stroller is too much for your baby, go slow. That is, with all the wheels locked in position, roll him back and forth steadily until he starts to slow down and drift off to sleep. This can be done with you sitting (on a park bench) or standing (still). On a nice, breezy day you can sit in a park reading a book or a magazine, talk to a friend, or just watch the world go by as your baby gently rocks to sleep.

TIP
145

Di-di-di-di-di-DEEE

A little game that no baby can resist is the di-di-di-di-di-DEEE game. You are undoubtedly saying to yourself right now, "Sheesh! Did I have to buy this book to learn about the di-di-di-di-di-DEEE game?" Well, there are one or two folks out there who haven't heard of it. For their benefit, it goes like this:

Take one crying baby who needs a diaper change and continues to cry even when you're done. With his legs and belly still exposed, run your fingers up from his toes, saying di-di-di-di-di-DEEE! until you get to his neck, where you may linger for a moment to tickle. Then repeat as needed until giggles replace cries.

For variety, start slowly at the toes, do a U-turn at the belly button, then go back up the neck.

TIP

Counting blue cars

The following advice is so deceptively simple that you just may not have considered it as a successful baby-calmer before.

When your toddler wakes up in a bad mood, go to the window and see what's happening in the world. Gasp and say "Ooh, look!" as you watch the goings-on below. If you're in an apartment, count the cars. (They need not be blue, but on some days maybe that's all she'll want to count.) If you're in the suburbs or country, watch the wind rustle leaves in the trees, or point out the neighbor's kitty. If you're facing a brick wall, try putting up a picture or a painting (an older sib's work is perfect for this) and get imaginative.

TIP

147

Call the "uh-oh" squad!

When minor bonks and bumps occur, it is important to establish yourself as a calm and collected adult who is concerned but not panicked. Babies pick up on emotional distress and amplify it right back at you. They also pick up on levelheadedness and can cool down right along with you. So when he takes a tumble (as he inevitably will), keep your wits about you, look for signs of significant injury, and say in a singsong voice, "Get the uh-oh squad! Uh-oh alert on (*your address here*)! Baby fall down go boom!" Then, smother him with kisses. His crying and pain may not end immediately, but you will have prevented the event from escalating into hysteria.

(Be warned—certain children have been known to utter "uh-oh!" as their first word as a result.)

Subscription cards

Every day you bring in the mail; and in with the bills, brochures, and magazines is anything *but* the letters from the friends who have long since deserted you and your baby. But there *are* lots of magazine subscription cards. And there are any number of ways to entertain a baby with subscription cards. You know, of course, that a cranky baby wants mommy time and doesn't want her to look at the mail.

Make a paper airplane out of the card. Or shooting baskets with crumpled cards (yelling "score" or "ouch, airball!" as appropriate). Or make a house of cards with them that baby can make "fall down go boom!" If you have some junk mail, baby can enjoy helping you shred it.

While you do this, you'll get to look through your mail, and baby will have a little fun.

TIP

149

Cozy, cozy crib

If your baby needs to fall asleep in your arms (not an ideal situation to begin with), you have probably faced the problem of getting him out of your arms and into bed. Nothing is going to wake 'em up faster than a cold sheet on a cold winter night. Then try getting your baby *back* to sleep or even *interested* in sleep.

In winter, try putting a heating pad or hot water bottle under the blanket for a few minutes before laying him down. Make the sheets and comforter nice and toasty, not overheated, put him down, and then take away the heating pad. And, for some reason unknown only to those in the under-two group, babies often sleep more easily when the air is a bit nippy.

TIP

150

Activity: rocker

After baby has gained a modest degree of upper body control (evidenced by getting into and out of a sitting position), she's ready for a rocking horse or an activity rocker. Rocking can work for cranky or bored babies in roughly the same way that a swing works—a little jiggling fun never hurt anyone.

Don't want to buy another thing? Practically every family with older children has some kind of rocker stored in a basement or attic. When you're ready for their next batch of hand-me-down baby clothes, ask if they have one of these hiding away. A little safety hint: Make sure that it's new enough to have a built-in seat belt.

TIP

151

Instant rattle

Maybe the world is waiting for a better mousetrap. Until then, it will have to settle for a better rattle. There's nothing wrong with the rattle you can get from the toy store, but why not make one yourself?

First, start with a one-pint clear plastic container of wonton soup. Call your favorite Chinese place or have your spouse bring it home from work. Drink the soup, clean the container, and set aside.

Second, feed your baby six to eight jars of baby food. This should *not* be given all at once. Clean out the jars and *save the lids*.

Finally, place the lids into the soup container and *voilà*! Instant rattle.

Calms one crier.

Mega-ball

A sixteen-inch ball is big, but not as big as a twenty-six-inch ball. Those are BIG. And a thirty-six-inch ball is, well, *BIG*! You can bounce it to him, and you can bounce him on it. You can kick it in the air and watch it knock over everything in sight (assuming you are willing to clean it all up afterwards). No bored, crying child can resist the play possibilities a really huge ball has to offer. They are available in catalogs and lots of toy stores and can be used in or out of the house. Look for one with a textured pattern to make it somewhat nonskid—especially useful when baby is on top.

"Hot!"

A nine-month-old doesn't know when she's getting into trouble; you do. Nor does a nine-month-old understand that the oven door she likes to open (now that she's developed the fine arts of crawling and pulling up) is going to make her come to grief.

One of the best concepts to introduce her to early is the word "hot!" Your tone of voice should cause her to take notice, as should your lightning-fast response of swooping down and rescuing her from the oven door. After a few times, a loud "hot!" may be all that it takes to stop her from ending up with a big, bad boo-boo.

TIP

154

Substitution

When your baby finally gets her crawling act into high gear, she will find inevitably all of her older brother's toys. At first, he'll think this is cute. But then *it* happens. She sets her sights on the blocks he's been stacking all afternoon into an architectural marvel to rival I. M. Pei's finest. The music of *Jaws* swells inexorably in the background, your baby girl closes in perilously on the heaven-reaching towers and buttresses, and big brother's wails of "Noooooo!" resonate through the playroom . . .

This is the time for you to teach big brother about the strategy of substitution. Let him pick out his sister's favorite stuffed animal or ball. Make sure he keeps it close at hand so that when she is bearing down like a killer shark on his engineering project, he will have bait to lure her away.

Diaper rash, part 1

There are two predominant kinds of diaper rash, a fungal infection and contact, or irritation, dermatitis (dermatitis means skin irritation). Both are irritating but usually not painful.

A fungal infection is most often caused by *Candida albicans*, which also causes oral thrush and vaginal infections in women. In babies it causes a bright red sheetlike rash with little red pinpoints (satellite lesions) at the edges. It starts off in small patches and creeps outward gradually. The treatment is an antifungal cream. Most are available without a prescription. Generally, a small amount is applied three or four times a day for several days until the rash clears (add another day for good measure). As always, follow the directions on the label.

Diaper rash, part 2

Contact dermatitis is less red than a fungal rash and is more likely to appear on the skin surfaces that are directly against the diaper surface. By contrast, fungal rashes are often deep within the moist creases, where fungi like to grow. The contact with the wet or soiled diaper surfaces causes the irritation rash and eventually causes skin breakdown and redness. Satellite lesions do not accompany a contact dermatitis.

Usually a cortisone cream (hydrocortisone 0.5 or 1 percent) applied three or four times a day is sufficient to heal the rash in a few days. After it heals, slather on Desitin, A&D ointment, or some other barrier cream (zinc oxide) to prevent the skin from coming into prolonged contact with the irritant, or change diapers more frequently.

If you can't tell the difference between a contact dermatitis and a fungal infection, or think it might be both (which is possible), use both ointments. Put the antifungal cream on with the first diaper change and the cortisone the next time, and alternate the two until the skin clears.

TIP

Sitting up

Crying can serve as a signal that your baby is growing up. When she develops the strength and coordination for sitting upright (at about four months), she will start crying from frustration at not being able to get to a sitting position by herself.

Sit her down, place one or two large pillows behind her, another one at each side to avoid tipping over, then give her an ample supply of toys for her to teethe on, turn back and forth in her hands, bang, or throw. With enough interesting objects close at hand, she can entertain herself for long periods at a time and free you to *momentarily* do whatever you need. Keep in mind that you want to be close enough to prop her back upright if she does a header and lands on her face.

Another caution: Keep a close eye on older sibs or playmates in the area who may either take her toys away or give her ones that are too small for her and could pose a choking hazard.

Nice, nice, nice, boo!

For the I-need-to-be-snuggled kind of cry, play this game:

Sit her in your lap, face-to-face, and take her wrists in your hands. Then have her hands stroke your cheeks, saying "Nice! Nice! Nice!" a few times, followed by a "Boo!" as you throw her hands up in the air. Do this several times, changing the number of times you say "Nice" and the surprise at the end. For instance, say "So big!" and open her arms up wide or "Nose!" and touch her finger to your nose. Or "Oops! Tickle!" and stuff her hands in her tummy.

Dads, make sure you've shaved before you try this, unless she doesn't mind rubbing her hands through steel wool.

TIP

Food allergy

As you start introducing new foods to your baby's diet, you also start introducing the chance that he may react to them. Symptoms of a food allergy include excess gas, diarrhea or mucusy stools, a scaly, red facial rash, and, of course, fussiness and crying.

Because this can occur in any child, introduce foods one at a time for the first several foods. Give at least three or four days between new foods to identify any reactions. Cereals are the safest to start with, followed by strained vegetables. Certain foods are more notoriously allergenic than others, such as egg whites, chocolate, nuts, wheat, tomatoes, and shellfish. Your doctor may recommend that you avoid these substances until your baby is older.

If you have a family history of asthma, eczema, or food sensitivity or your baby has already exhibited any of these signs, go cautiously, and consult with your doctor. Some offices have nutritionists or nurses available who specialize in dealing with these matters if you are having more than your share of food allergy problems. Most have, at the very least, instructional pamphlets or videos from the AAP or other authoritative organizations.

TIP

Lactose intolerance

Unlike milk allergy, inability to digest lactose, the main sugar present in milk, is quite common. Lactose is composed of two paired simple sugars, glucose and galactose. Lactose is split into single components by the enzyme lact*ase*, and these sugars are absorbed from the intestinal tract. A few children have a congenital, primary lactose intolerance, but more commonly it develops as a brief response to a gastrointestinal infection. However, children from three to six years old may begin to show signs of *permanent* intolerance as they lose the ability to digest lactose. About 33 percent of black children and 10 percent of white children have permanent lactose intolerance.

The treatment, as for milk allergy, is exclusion of milk products from the diet. Some products with predigested milk sugars (such as yogurt) are available, and other products claim to replace the missing enzyme. If these work, they can be safely used. However, a variety of other foods can be offered to provide needed calcium and vitamins.

TIP

Fever, part 2

Fever in an older infant is different than fever in a new baby. Under the age of about six to ten weeks, fever may be the first and only sign of a serious infection. Later, fever is more common and more likely to represent a minor viral problem rather than a serious bacterial infection.

When fever develops, there are usually clues as to its cause. For example, a runny nose and/or cough are signs of an upper respiratory infection, and vomiting and diarrhea are signs of a gastrointestinal bug. If the fever is under 104°F and your baby seems comfortable after taking an appropriate amount of Tylenol or ibuprofen, the odds are good that he has something minor that will last only a few days.

One way to gauge the seriousness of a fever is to see how your baby is acting when his temperature is back to normal. If he seems okay, then the chances are good that he *is* okay. If his fever comes down but he still seems to be irritable or unhappy, then you should think about having his doctor check him.

Truly worrisome signs include: having no energy even when the temperature comes down, respiratory distress, diminished urination, a pale or mottled skin color, or obvious signs of pain.

TIP

Colds

A cold is a viral upper respiratory infection. It is characterized by fever of anywhere from 101ºF to 104ºF, a clear nasal discharge that typically becomes thicker and greener by the end of the cold, a moist cough, a poor appetite, and crankiness. An ear infection may develop after a few days if the nasal congestion backs up into the middle ear cavity. A sinus infection may develop if the congestion is green and thick for more than a day or two.

Nasal decongestants or antihistamines are very rarely helpful for a young baby and are usually useless for older babies. In babies less than a year old, an antihistamine may make them even more cranky and unhappy.

The only things you can do are make sure that she is comfortable. Cuddle her, push lots of fluids, and give Tylenol or ibuprofen for fevers. Don't expect her to eat much until she's feeling better.

Antibiotics do not make colds go away, so I suggest you only call your doctor if it seems like something more than just a common cold. Here's one last clue that a cold is really just a cold: Every other baby you know has similar symptoms.

TIP

Teething, part 1

Typically teething begins at age six to seven months. The symptoms vary from child to child, but the ones that are most common include:

- Crying, irritability
- Drooling
- Biting
- A chin rash from the drooling
- Ear tugging
- Difficulty feeding due to the pain

There is absolutely *no* accepted medical data that shows that the eruption of teeth through the gum line causes fever. If the baby's temperature is above 101°F, it is from another cause.

This table is only a very rough guide. There is a wide range in normal values for eruption of both the primary and permanent teeth.

AVERAGE AGE OF TOOTH ERUPTION

Tooth	Months	Tooth	Months	Tooth	Months
Central incisor	6 (4–12)	Canine	18 (13–19)	Second Molar	24 (20–33)
Lateral incisor	8 (6–16)	First molar	12 (10–19)		

TIP

164

Viral rashes

Most viruses that children get tend to result in fever, crankiness, and slightly diminished appetite (although they usually make up in fluids what they don't eat) for a few days, along with a few select other symptoms such as a cough, vomiting, runny nose, etc. A smaller percentage of viral infections may produce a rash, which may serve to identify a specific viral infection (e.g., chicken pox) or a nonspecific infection. The characteristics of this latter kind of rash are:

- Pink spots, not red or purple.
- Small spots the size of a "period" on a page.
- The spots blanch on pressure. Roll a glass over an affected area. If the spot disappears with gentle pressure, it is "blanching." Serious rashes are nonblanching.
- The spots do not itch.

Rashes that do not exhibit these characteristics should probably be investigated, particularly if they appear along with fever and irritability.

TIP

Dehydration

Crying without tears after bouts of vomiting and/or diarrhea is a sign of dehydration. You might find that your baby is peeing less often, has stringy saliva in a dry mouth (dry lips are not specific for dehydration—they get that way from cold and/or dry air), or that her eyes look sunken. Usually she has no energy at this point either.

Most of the time, a trip to the ER is necessary for a course of IV rehydration. However, *if* everyone in the neighborhood has the same bug (and stomach viruses often run rampant in a community), *if* you know that your baby got it from someone else with the same symptoms, and *if* you can spend lots of time with her, you may not need to spend several hours in the same ER as everyone else who has the same thing. What you *will* need to do is give her sips of a balanced rehydrating solution (Rehydralyte, Infalyte, Pedialyte, *not* apple juice or water) every five minutes or so until she seems to be improving, which may take an hour or two.

If your child is *developing* a stomach flu that may lead to dehydration, you can feed her in the same slow, patient way and avoid the kind of moderately severe dehydration described above.

TIP

Sunburn

Babies are far more susceptible to the effects of the sun than are grown-ups. They have thinner skin, which is less able to block the deleterious effects of ultraviolet rays, and they are also more prone to heat injuries like heatstroke. A baby who has been exposed to the sun for too long may also become dehydrated.

Sunburn is a thermal burn, just like spilling hot water. There are degrees of burn: a first-degree burn is puffy and red and may develop after half an hour of exposure on a bright day (less in fair-skinned babies). A second-degree burn is accompanied by blisters and is more serious and more painful.

Treating a sunburn requires constant cool compresses (a washcloth bathed in cool water). Do not use ice. In addition, a moisturizing or lubricating lotion such as Noxzema or calamine lotion may be used. Occlusive ointments such as zinc oxide or Vaseline are a bad idea because they trap moisture and do not permit fresh air to come into contact with the burned skin.

For more severe sunburns, a steroid cream may be in order. Check with your doctor.

And, as always, push lots of fluids to make up for the body fluid lost through the skin, and give Tylenol for pain.

TIP

Chemicals in the eye

Occasionally, a chemical such as soap, shampoo, household cleaner, or a cooking ingredient (such as oils or spices) will splash in a baby's eye. Most household detergents are dilute enough so as not to cause harm, although they do produce significant irritation. In the event of a splash to the eye, you should flush out the eye and then call the poison control center or your doctor.

Eye irrigation is safe and effective but may require two people, one to hold the baby still and a second person to pour water on the eye. The baby should be held on his side with the affected eye downward. Then take a cup of lukewarm water (room temperature) and pour it from the nasal corner of the eye so that it flows to the outer corner. Do this several times, or hold the baby under a gently flowing water tap. Water is the best means of neutralizing any chemical (*never* add an acid to neutralize a base or vice versa), and most foreign debris should be washed away as well. Following this, the eye will most likely appear pink, but your baby should be more comfortable—once he calms down.

TIP

168

Stranger anxiety

Every parent and pediatrician has seen this: Baby is clinging happily to mom until she gets face-to-face near another adult. Then she clutches mom, draws her legs tight, and makes faces—scared faces. One move closer and she dissolves in tears.

Stranger anxiety is a developmental milestone. It represents baby's awareness that her parents are very special people to her and that everyone else in the universe is potentially the Unabomber. She gets all her needs fulfilled by her parents; no one else, even grandma, can compete.

This is not the time to try to force her to smile or be sociable to appease grandma. Baby has made up her mind, and the best thing to do is leave her alone until her perspective changes. Once stranger anxiety starts, it can be tough to bring in a new baby-sitter; if this can be avoided, stick with the ones she knows.

While your baby's stranger anxiety may only last a few months, it can continue well up to your baby's second birthday.

TIP

Stranger dislike

Your baby may have a very good reason for crying when Aunt Adrian picks him up for a session of kissy-kissy face that has nothing to do with stranger anxiety: Aunt Adrian may have a bad habit of wearing perfume by the bucketful, or she may have a lingering cigarette odor that makes your little guy nauseous. If you detect a scent when you give your visitor a peck on the cheek, it may help smooth relations between Auntie and baby to tell her about it.

In the same vein, Uncle Dmitri may have too firm a grip when snuggling up to his favorite nephew. If he is a frequent visitor, your boy will quickly learn that he is in for a roughing up and will cry in anticipation. Once again, an early clue might be the vigorous way he grabs *you* for a bear hug.

TIP

170

Babies just wanna play all day

At six months old, baby is ready to play. Put yourself in her position: She's fed and rested; she'll want to play a nice game of peekaboo with her mommy. But mommy is in the bathroom or on the telephone. Never fear. Baby knows there is one way to get her attention: waa-a-a-aaah! As soon as mommy appears, "All better!"

Once she's smiling, don't turn your back and go back to whatever it was you were doing. She wants to play with you! This means some prioritizing on your part. Do the cooking later. Make your calls tomorrow. Play with your baby.

The same thing applies for the baby who cries while she's being toted around on your hip. Sure, she's being jostled and jiggled around, but how about some face time?

Choking, part 1

Once babies develop the power to move around in their own environment, the biggest thing you need to protect them against is their own curiosity. Since this manifests itself as exploring with the hand and mouth, anything that *can* go into their mouth *will*.

If a baby chokes on an object that completely blocks his airway, he will make absolutely no sound because his airway is completely blocked, and he cannot cry for help (another reason to keep your baby always in sight).

Crying from choking on an object that only partially blocks the airway (either from sitting above the vocal cords or from passing deeper into the lungs and blocking a smaller airway) is sharp, sudden in onset, and distressed. Your baby may appear pale, mottled, or blue, and he will grasp at his throat.

Performing the Heimlich maneuver is critical for a completely or partially obstructed airway. If the object has fallen deeper into the lungs, you will need to go to the ER and it will have to be removed immediately.

TIP

172

Choking, part 2

When it comes to feeding babies, there are certain foods that pose choking hazards. Hard, small foods about an inch in diameter pose the highest risk and should be avoided until she is old enough to chew and swallow efficiently. In this regard, beware of the older sibling with a bag of carrots or raisins who may try to feed baby. Some foods that pose choking hazards include:

- Peanuts
- Raw vegetable cubes
- Hot dogs
- Whole grapes
- Raisins
- Hard candies
- M&Ms

Song: "The Wheels on the Bus"

There's a great pop-up book that goes along with this, illustrated by Paul Zelinsky.

The wheels on the bus go round and round
   (fingers trace a circle in the air)
Round and round, round and round
The wheels on the bus go round and round
All through the town.

The wipers on the bus go swish, swish, swish…
   (wipe fingers back and forth)
The door on the bus goes open and shut…
   (hands open and shut—play peekaboo)
The horn on the bus goes beep, beep, beep…
   (palms out, as if honking a horn)
The seats on the bus goes bump, bump, bump…
   (jiggle baby on your knees)
The baby on the bus says waah, waah, waah!…
   (ball up fists in eyes and pretend to cry)
The mommy on the bus says I love you…
   (hug baby)

TIP

174

Mommy's home: decompress!

Did you ever notice how your baby dissolves into a torrent of wailing and tears the moment you see him after a day away from him? His caregiver reports that he was fine all afternoon, ate his lunch, napped well, and had a poopy diaper—a perfect angel. So what gives?

What gives is that he is trying to do two things at once. First, he wants you to make up for all the play and face time you've missed by being away all day. And second, he wants you to think that there's no way he can handle another day of your absence, and if you don't want to find a basket case when you come home tomorrow, you'd better *stay* home tomorrow.

There's nothing wrong with lavishing a little extra attention on baby when you get home (it might just be the best antidote for another lousy day in the trenches), but don't feel so guilty that you rethink your career or economic goals.

TIP

175

Fears

Just as your baby may get spooked by the sight of strangers, there will also come a time when sudden, loud noises frighten him: Vacuum cleaners may not soothe him now, but may set off a crying jag, as does loud music or a barking dog.

Although this is a transient phase, it is important to get through it successfully. If you know what will scare him, avoid it. Walk on the other side of the street if he is scared by a noisy dog. In some cases, when a noise is unavoidable (such as a doorbell or vacuum cleaner), hug him close and show that *you* are not scared. This may help him to overcome the fear and may teach him a valuable lesson in accepting new situations.

Fears of this sort are not the same thing as phobias, which arrive in about a year or so.

Is baby home?

Babies usually indicate that they've awakened from a nap by crying, and ours often carried on in a cranky, bad mood for long afterward. The trick to getting them in a good mood was to get them smiling from the start.

When I heard our baby cry, I would stand outside the bedroom door and knock loudly, open the door quickly, and say "Knock, knock. Is Baby home?" and quickly shut the door. Then I knock again and say "Baby? Has anyone seen Baby?"

They are startled at first (and forget to cry for a second) and quickly get in the mood for the game. For variety, I would knock, pause, knock again a little louder, then pause again, and knock again. After a few knocks, our boys were always full of smiles. Then, of course, came the diaper changing and the tears again.

TIP

Rolling over

The first time your baby rolls over is a major milestone, and if you're not there to witness it, you'll *hear* about it. He will cry because he's stuck in a new position and can't get out of it. (Here's a great idea for a baby shirt: "I've rolled over and I can't get up.") Turning over takes work. It often only results when he's looking for a toy (such as a mobile overhead) or hears your voice.

Interestingly, babies seem to be turning over at a later age in recent years. In the early '90s, clear evidence emerged that SIDS deaths were more common in babies who slept on their bellies. As a result, the AAP recommended that babies sleep in the supine position (on their backs), or at least propped on their sides. This has resulted in fewer SIDS deaths and in delayed motor skills. Pushing off from the belly onto the back is easier than rolling onto the stomach, and more babies are now doing this later. Never fear, by eight to nine months, your baby will probably be absolutely everywhere underfoot, and you'll start looking back on these first months as the "easy" months. (Oh, yes, you will!)

TIP

178

Head banging

Babies may not cry *because* of head banging, but they cry during it. This bizarre behavior is normal in the second half of the first year, is probably more common in boys than girls, and is an attempt at self-pacifying. Babies like being rocked and rhythmic patting—something they become accustomed to when you pat them to wind down. So if little Tiger is left to his own devices, he may turn to some rhythmic rocking of his own and discover that lightly bopping his head against the side of the crib feels good. Since the motivation for this behavior is irritability, crankiness, or mild displeasure, it is not unusual for him to cry while he does it. If you haven't done so already, this might be a good time to put up the crib's bumpers.

Jumping seat

The jumping seat is a valuable tool that should be standard equipment for any family with an active baby. A seat is attached to a long strap and tight spring and can be connected to most doorframes that have an upper molding. By adjusting the height so that the baby's feet just rest on the floor, the baby can hop up and down and work off lots of energy. If you place this in the kitchen or some other working part of the house, she may try and propel herself to you, swing back, and in general have one grand old time trying to reach you. (Sure, sure the instructions will tell you that they're not supposed to swing from a jumper, but just try and stop them.) Put in a crying baby, and you'll pull out a happy camper.

These are widely available and cost around $40.

I see me

A different spin on the peekaboo game is the "Where's baby?" game. If baby is cranky, try walking her past a large mirror and letting her see herself. Give a little gasp: "Where's baby? I see me! I see baby!" Babies quickly learn when the face they are seeing is their own, and they usually hold their cute pudgy face in the same high regard as do their mom and dad. Repeat this a couple of times, and you will watch the tears dry up and the smiles come out when you play this little game.

It may even help at times when they aren't just waking up: A baby who sees her crying face in the mirror doesn't know whether to laugh at the sad face or keep on crying.

I see me me me me me

If your bathroom has mirrors that are at right angles to one another (i.e., a mirror over the sink and a mirror over the medicine cabinet), a sure way to grab baby's attention is to open the cabinet mirror to create a circular, receding series of reflections. In our house this was fondly known as "so many babies." Playing peekaboo this way takes on a whole bigger dimension, as an infinite number of babies are hiding and seeking.

Caution: This may actually scare the bejesus out of some babies the first time around, so you may want to try this first when they are in a good mood.

TIP

182

Naps

A baby's "I need a nap" cry is usually quite distinctive. It's neither loud nor soft and seems to come from the back of the throat. He can't sustain interest in food or toys, and his eyes are drooping as he's whimpering.

Studies on sleep in newborns and babies have demonstrated that a three-month-old requires about sixteen hours of sleep a day, half of it during the day, half at night. By six months, the daytime component has dropped to about four to five hours, or two to three naps.

Getting baby to sleep is the hard part. If your baby won't go down for a nap easily, he will eventually go down the hard way: by crying it out. To improve the chances of doing it the easy way, the steps are similar for getting him to sleep for the night:

- Lead up to it with a predictable, quiet routine: feeding/nursing, a story, a blanket.
- Keep the noise and lights low.
- Be on the lookout for a baby who is ready to give up one of the daily naps. If he's not tired and looks like he's having fun, don't force the issue.

TIP

183

Peekaboo

Playing games is what having a baby is all about. Once she's gotten tired of sitting and playing with all the toys you've placed at her feet or in her lap, play with her face to face. Peekaboo is a great game for a baby who is just beginning to learn "object permanence," that is, that an object still exists even when it disappears from sight. Prior to this stage, if something was not in her field of vision, it simply didn't exist. When you hide your face, you can tell that she has achieved this milestone by her efforts to look around for you.

It's great for crying because she's fascinated by your face and has a major interest in seeing it reappear. She'll be so focused on the activity ("Hey, I think I know what made this work last time; I hope I can do it again!—There!! It worked!!) that she'll forget to cry.

TIP
184

Music for adults that kids love

B abies love music, particularly when crying. Music is a funny thing. What is it about some songs that make them cutting edge at one time and baby songs a generation later? Think of some early Beatles songs or most doo-wop, and you'll get the picture. Your baby has no sense of music history, but smiles instinctively when she hears certain songs. Soft, higher-pitched (feminine) voices accompanied by cheerful piano or woodwind instruments are essential components of most baby-song tapes and CDs and are available in every style of music. Play them when she's happy, and they may cheer her up when she's crying.

If you can't tolerate the thought of endless, droning repetitions of "Six Little Ducks That I Once Knew," you can certainly try to expose her to the B-52's; or R.E.M. Songs like "Rock Lobster" or "It's the End of the World as We Know It" have a cross-generational appeal.

TIP

185

A Flemish song

Certain songs work like a magic charm on certain babies. This one cast an unbreakable spell on our Nathan. He was so bamboozled he could never quite bring himself to cry the same way again—for at least another fifteen minutes:

Han	shes	droye	kuku	baka	floye
C	E	G E	F D	F	A G
1	1	1 1½	½ 1	1	1½ 1

Han	shes	droye	kuku	bake	vees
C	E	GE	FD	D	C
1	1	1 1½	½ ½	½	1 ½

A rough translation of this is: "Hands are turning." It is sung while twisting your hand with the palm open and fingers half closed.

My brother-in-law Harold translates it this way: "We are so poor, we can't afford toys; we are so poor, so we play with our hands."

Funny voices

You need not be a master of disguise to come up with a few funny voices that your baby will enjoy. Work them in during playtime when she's in a good mood, and she may respond to them better when she's in a foul mood. Some classics are:

- Boris Badinov ("Time for moose and squirrel to have lit-tle *surprise*!)
- Bugs Bunny ("What's up, doc?")
- Peter Lorre (Lately known as Stimpy. Or Ren.)
- Barney ('super-dee-duper!')
- Dave Letterman's "dumb guy" voice. (I assume that you were up this late during the first few months and had a chance to watch some late-night TV.)
- Marcel Marceau (Uh—oops! Never mind.)

TIP

187

Teething, part 2

Teething babies are miserable and uncomfortable. Any number of parents I have seen swear that the best thing they have tried is to have their baby chew on a frozen bagel. It won't break up into particles that can be inhaled and lasts for at least half an hour.

You should not try frozen vegetables, such as peas, that can break up into small pieces or any other food that you don't want your baby to eat when it thaws. Nor should you apply ice directly to the gum: That will be painfully cold itself and can cause frostbite if you leave it on long enough. Wrap some crushed ice in a plastic bag, and then wrap a washcloth around the bag—it's unwieldy, but baby might actually let you do this.

Pain medicine—Tylenol or ibuprofen—in recommended doses should not be forgotten, either.

TIP

188

Finger games

Cave paintings from France that date back to the end of the last ice age have been deciphered to show mommies playing this game with their babies.

Open them and shut them, (your hands)
Open them and shut them,
Put them in your lap!
Creep them, creep them (walk them up her legs)
Give a little clap!
Open wide—your little mouth
But do – not – let – them – in! (Wave your finger
   back and forth in front of your mouth.)

TIP

189

Install a car sunshade

A car ride won't be an effective soother if your baby is sitting under the window like a plant in a hothouse. Use a roll-down model with suction cups, or get a sheet of adherent dark transparent plastic. In any case, don't compromise your or your baby's safety by placing a truly opaque shade in front of a window that you will need to see through to navigate in traffic.

TIP

190

Make the car seat comfy

Another car comfort adjustment that may head off crying is to readjust the shoulder straps of her car seat. They may have fit her fine as a newborn, but she has grown by leaps and bounds. Get a set of shoulder strap covers, so that when the car decelerates, there is padding against her chest, not the firm fabric of the strap itself. If you ever see a faint V-shaped bruising or chafing along baby's chest, it is not alien possession, most likely the shoulder harness is too tight.

TIP

191

Toss those tears away

My mother-in-law swears that she has done this to all of her grandchildren. She scrunches her fingers up in front of their face and grabs baby's tears. "Don't cry for grandma, grandma loves you!" And then she says "I'm going to throw those tears away. Say good-bye! Say bye-bye to those tears!" Then she throws the tears out the window. Then she, herself, starts to cry and tosses the tears away.

This may be the secret that grandmothers have been harboring for all of these years, so don't let on that you know.

TIP

192

Snacks

Babies do not always operate on a three-square-meals-a-day battery. (Few adults do, when it comes right down to it.) Now that your child is eating solid foods, he might cry between meals if he is hungry. He may require several more smaller feedings throughout the day. It is a sound idea to try to organize a couple of them into a bigger meal, but small snacks serve multiple purposes beyond keeping baby's tummy full. Playing with food is his way of exploring his surroundings. He learns about the textures of different foods, and he learns fine motor skills by accomplishing the task of placing the food in his mouth. Just watch an eight-month-old try to get a Cheerio into his mouth. (The gross motor skill development needed for flinging food across the room is something he will value more than you, perhaps, but it may pay off if there is a football scout in the area.) If you are having trouble weaning him from the breast or bottle, snacking also represents another new opportunity for him to learn how to gratify his oral fixation.

TIP

The diaper song

I have a hunch that this is a dad thing. My boys used to quiet down when, as I began to change their diapers, I started to sing our diaper song (to the tune of Tah-rah-rah-Boom-de-ay):

> *I-i-i-i-it's stinky* diap-y *time,*
> *It's stinky* diap-y *time,*
> *It's stinky diap-y time*
> *It's stin-ky DIAP-y time.*

This was followed by a quick rendition of:

> *Stinky-stinky poo-POO! Stinky-stinky poo-POO!*
> (to a sort of conga-type beat).

These songs worked best upon waking from a nap, when they didn't quite know what they wanted, and it started them off on the right foot.

Make a tape

Sure, you can be two places at once: Just record a tape of you performing your baby's favorite songs (or stories, for older children). It may be an ideal way for you to soothe baby while you work and can only keep half an eye on him. However, it may not be the best way to send him off to sleep, since it creates a bewildering situation of not knowing when mommy or daddy is really there.

If you are a parent who feels deprived of playing a greater role because you have to work outside the home, this can be a good way to get your child to bond with you during office hours.

Grab daddy's glasses

Why do babies like to pull off daddy's glasses? Because they can. The first time that our Zoe pulled off my glasses, she was crying and flailing her arms, and suddenly, miraculously, she had this *thing* in her hands that once was part of daddy's face. She stopped crying and waved it about. Alas, in a few moments it went crashing to the floor, and she resumed her wailing. She soon began to consciously reach for the glasses. Now, every chance she gets, she grabs my glasses off my face and giggles and shrieks in delight.

A couple of cautions: Make sure her nails are clipped to avoid scratches, and be sure your lenses are an unbreakable plastic. And don't let her get the earpiece in her eyes.

TIP

196

More Puppet Games

Just like puppet games for the under-one set are a surefire way to grab a baby's attention, they are also a wonderful way for a toddler to work off some anxiety by making him an active participant. Use puppet play to let him express latent fears or frustrations.

> *Elephant* (left-hand puppet, grumpy voice): *Hi, Mrs. Winnipissaukee! I want to play with Big Boy Jujube again!*
>
> *Mrs. Winnipissaukee* (right-hand puppet, squeaky voice): *Will you play nicely with his toys?*
>
> *Elephant: Oh I love his toys! And he's such a good sharer, too!*
>
> *Your son: No! Don't let him! He steals my toys and then breaks them just like*
>
> _____
>
> (big sister/brother's name)!

This primitive version of play therapy often works wonders. It focuses his vague anxieties into specific fears that he can tell you about. Usually it's easy to provide reassurance about whatever is on his mind: separation fears, toy ownership, etc.

For working moms (and dads, too)

Your little woogums may typically fall apart around lunchtime, after a morning of play and a nap. If you're not too far from home, do lunch with *him* instead of the client or the office staff. This is a good tonic for you as much as the baby and certainly provides more of a lift than just a check-in phone call (at least until the day arrives when video-conferencing is more widespread).

Crying at the sight of daddy

Dads sometimes get thrown out of the game just for making an appearance. In most major league sports, you have to commit an offense to get ejected; but at home, the ref (baby) may toss you out just for showing up.

What's up with *that*?

To borrow a line from Woody Allen, don't take rejection as a sign of rejection.

Let's say that dad comes home from a long day at work and wants to unwind by playing with his baby. This involves fancy flying, dancing, or other fun roughhousing. If baby has had a long day himself, he just may not be in the mood. He's probably cranky at dinnertime, and being tossed about when he's hungry and tired may not appeal to him. Once he knows that the routine for dad's return means a lot of nausea-inducing aerial stunts, it's no surprise that he gets upset.

So take it easy when you get home. Sit and read a story, give a bath, or start dinner. Make it a mellow moment rather than a grand, hectic entrance.

TIP

Knee games

Bounce her (gently! and never after a feeding!) on your knees in time to a favorite song: "The Noble Duke of York" (sung to the tune of "The Farmer in the Dell")

The Noble Duke of York. (bounce three times)
He had ten thousand men. (bounce three more times)
He marched them up to the top of the hill (gently toss her up)
And marched them down again. (drop her between your legs)
'Cuz when you're up you're up. (faster tempo—toss her up again)
And when you're down you're down. (drop her down again)
And when you're only halfway up you're neither up nor down. (toss halfway up, then all the way, then down)
He marched them to the left. (bounce baby to left)
He marched them to the right. (bounce baby to right)
He even marched them upside down. (turn baby upside down)
Oh what a silly sight!

TIP

200

Photo gallery

When you're away from home—at work, working out, whatever—leave your baby's caregiver with a favorite photo gallery for baby. It is probably best to make up a small album of doubles so that the pictures can get smeared, torn, and drooled on. Make sure there are lots of pics of mommy and baby, mommy and daddy, sibs (if any), and grandparents. This way your baby's caregiver can tell lots of stories about each family member to pass the time to calm a "where-*is*-everybody?" anxiety attack.

You might also make a tape of mommy singing or daddy telling a story to create a multimedia virtual-reality experience. (When not even that works, let the caregiver know that it's okay to page/call you.)

TIP

201

Toy rotation

Do you have more toys than you know what to do with? More than your baby can play with in a week? When he has so many toys to choose from, he may be less interested in many of them, and it can be tough—and frustrating—to find that single favorite toy he really wants. This leads to,—surprise!—more tears.

The solution to overchoice is to warehouse all but a select few toys—preferably ones he doesn't usually remember to play with. Give him a week with them and then rotate. Send them back to the storage room, pick out some new ones, and they will all seem fresh and new. You will never run out of toys to offer for those bored, cranky days, and you'll also cut down on clutter. He'll never notice that you have thinned the herd.

Bike trailer

For athletic, outdoorsy parents, there are athletic, outdoorsy crying solutions.

Bicycle riding is one of the most healthful activities you can do with a baby. It is of course too early to start your future Tour de France champion on his own bike, but you can still introduce him to the pleasures of the open road. As soon as he is capable of sitting up unassisted, prop him in the back of a bicycle trailer. Like a car ride for colicky young infants, this can offer a full sensory experience for a cranky or bored baby. Bike trailers are durable and constructed very thoughtfully. They offer seat belts, bug screens, as well as splash covers and canopies. Once baby's old enough for his own bicycle, your legs will be strong enough to take a shot at the Tour de France yourself, and the resale value is unmatched (for the trailer, that is).

TIP

203

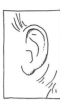

Ear care

If your baby is crying and you think that it might be an ear infection, call your doctor. Don't try to diagnose an ear infection at home by yourself. I have a top-ten list of reasons why home diagnosis is a bad idea:

1. Learning the difference between a normal and infected ear takes a *lot* of experience.
2. If you look when he is crying, the ear can appear red just from crying.
3. Your baby will probably forgive you— one day—but why be the bad guy?
4. You will need someone else to hold him, so you turn two people into the enemy.
5. If you wrongly diagnose the ear as normal, your baby spends an extra day crying and unhappy.
6. If you wrongly see an infection, you subject yourself to unnecessary antibiotics.
7. Whoa! Forget #6. You can't prescribe antibiotics even if you're right.
8. If there's a lot of wax, you won't see the whole eardrum.
9. Two words: Ruptured eardrum.
10. Your baby's doctor needs to eat, too.

TIP

204

The play yard: do's

Once your baby is beyond the colicky phase, some crying episodes are relatively predictable. Waking up from a nap in a bad mood can be one of these routine events.

It may take very little to turn his mood around, especially when he is in control of a few gross motor skills, such as head control and maintaining an upright posture. Set up a play yard stocked with toys, books, and stuffed animals. Make it a calm, fun environment for someone whose agenda includes lots of arm waving, bouncing on his tush, and flinging toys. The gates themselves should conform to safety regulations of the JPMA (Juvenile Products Manufacturing Association). Those sold in stores or catalogs all have such certification. (Just check.)

Even if he doesn't crawl yet, the gates should be fully closed. You never know when the crawling milestone will arrive, and you don't want it to arrive, literally, with a bang. Also: Don't leave pillows in there that can be stacked, crawled on, and provide a nice ramp to climb out.

Then: Get in and play with her in her world every once in awhile.

TIP

205

Not you!

Dads and baby-sitters, this one's for you: Sometimes no one but mommy will do. Upon waking up from a nap, for example, she may begin crying and keep it up even after her diaper is changed. She just ate less than half an hour ago, so you know she's not hungry. Offer her a toy, and she cries even louder. Your clue that she wants mommy (and nothing else) is the way she looks around the corner as you carry her from bedroom to family room to kitchen.

If mom happens to be there and takes baby from you, watch for this performance: Baby screws her face up, lets out one or two more wails for good measure, then settles into mom's arms and gives you a big syrupy smile. Don't buy it. She was crying to get dad to do her bidding and she just won. Remember this moment for when she's sixteen and asking you to please let her have a driver's license.

If mom is gone, try to avoid taking her to those rooms where she might expect to find her. Try distracting her with food or toys. If all else fails, try getting mom on the phone.

3–12 MONTHS: BABYHOOD

Get down!

It's easy to carry over the habit, picked up during baby's first few months, of toting him around on your hip every time he gets cranky. Two factors combine to create this: his desire to be held; your desire to calm him. By six months of age, when this is a reflex, you've created a Klingon—a fifteen-pound pink package that clings to your hip. A baby who has just had a meal, a nap, and a diaper change should, by most rational standards, have it all. Not quite. He may *settle* for being carried, but what he may really want is to play—with you. He may want to show off that he knows how to spit or razz or whatever new skill he's mastered. So if you put him down to play and then turn your back on him, you can expect tears. Get down on the floor with him. One great baby game is "piggies in the nose." Sing "piggies in the nose, piggies in the nose (squish his toes into his nose and cheeks), fly away *home* (clap hands)!" Give him a toy and show him a new way to play with it. Let him try to pull himself up or roll over. Put the time to good use. You will encourage his motor development and may even get to catch a milestone in the making.

TIP

207

Watch the snacking

Food-for-crying is a *solution* in the first months of life. When it is a *reflex* in later months, you may be creating problems.

Never substitute snacks for playing. If he's cranky and bored, he probably wants a little time to play with you. Putting him in a highchair and supplying him with some Cheerios may quiet him down a little, but after a few months of this, you may start wondering why he's so heavy to carry around and won't calm down until you put some food in front of him.

Once again, it's a matter of prioritizing. There are always missions you have to accomplish, but it never hurts to put your little guy or gal first. As with most reflex solutions, it started out honestly enough. But as your baby's needs change, so should your responses.

TIP

208

Taking a fall

Don't panic when your pre-toddler falls. Assess the situation before deciding whether or not there's anything to worry about, especially if you have not witnessed the actual incident. She will cry no matter what, and the more startled she is—not necessarily the more she hurts—the more likely she is to take a deep breath before she lets out a wail. Let her have her cry first, and be sure to give her lots of sympathy: "Oh, baby fall down and go boom!"

Once she has settled down, which can take several minutes, do a systems check. Feel for lumps, bumps, and bruises. If she takes more than five minutes or so to calm down and she seems hurt in a specific location, think about calling your doctor. If she has hit her head, there are certain signs (i.e persistent vomiting, lethargy, irritability and/or a high pitched cry) to clue you in to a potential injury.

If there seems to be nothing seriously injured, but she's still upset (and a substantial amount of research literature indicates that injuries after falling from standing or sofa height are usually trivial), give her a little Tylenol or ibuprofen for pain. Reward *yourself* a little, also, for handling the situation well and also for teaching your baby that you can *both* handle these little tumbles.

TIP

Read a book

Try reading a book to your crying baby. It's never too early to start one of the best habits of a lifetime. Use a chubby board book; there are zillions that have one brightly colored picture and one word per page, e.g., Dog, Toes, Baby. Invariably, at this age, her first instinct will be to grab the book and put it in her mouth. Let her. That's why they're made of cardboard. When she gets tired, frustrated, or otherwise finished with it, pick up a new one. As she gets older, she will become much more interested with what's on the page for its own sake. In the meantime, she will learn that reading a book in mommy or daddy's lap is a very satisfying activity in its own right.

She is probably absorbing far more than you give her credit for. This is a great way to boost language and comprehension skills.

TIP

210

Backpack

When your baby won't stop crying unless she's right next to you, and you can't neglect your daily duties any more, strap her on to your back. Superwoman doesn't wear a cape, she wears a backpack baby. At about six months, your baby should have enough head and neck support to permit carrying her around in a backpack.

Backpacks come in a variety of sizes, prices, and complexities. (There are even Elmo backpacks.) One feature to look for is a baby compartment that zips in and out. This way, you'll be able to wrestle her into the leg holes without having to struggle with the entire backpack. It converts a two-person job into one that can be managed by one crazed, tired mom.

TIP

Nap at the right time

Don't let your baby take a catnap if you can avoid it. The quickest way to make a baby genuinely irritable is to let him sleep for fifteen to thirty minutes and then wake him up. This kind of on-again, off-again sleep plays havoc with baby's natural sleep rhythms and is worse than no sleep at all.

Your baby needs about fourteen to fifteen hours of sleep a day and gets most of it (ten to eleven hours) at night after about age two months. Two long naps during the day meets a physiological need for the remaining few hours of sleep much better than several, shorter catnaps. This makes timing crucial. Don't expect a hungry baby to nap for long, nor one with a wet or stinky diaper. Car naps are inevitable, but try to transfer him in and out of the car seat without waking him up. If he wakes easily, then try to avoid short car trips when you know he'll be sleepy.

TIP

Breath-holding spells

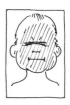

Breath-holding spells are the single most frightening experiences a parent will ever witness. It starts when a baby is crying (usually from anger) and begins to hyperventilate, drawing in bigger and longer breaths until there is just a stone cold silence and the baby turns blue. At the very end, before the baby resumes breathing again, he may twitch or jerk, making the whole episode look very much like a seizure. Two-thirds of *all* babies who do this begin before their first birthday.

Breath-holding usually cannot be stopped or derailed once it has started. The only thing to do is to prevent it from occurring in the first place. Since it usually occurs when he is tired or overstimulated, try to maintain a calm, quiet environment for those times when he's due to go to sleep. If the problem is a simple one to resolve in his favor, give him the victory. Not every issue should be a battleground.

Even though you don't want to teach him he can dominate you by holding his breath, this is an extremely frightening behavioral response to a normal frustration. Let it slide until you have some solid recommendations from your doctor of how best to manage it.

TIP

Walkers

Don't ever put your baby in a walker. Period. A baby who cries from boredom or who wants your attention should never be placed into a walker no matter how much he or she might enjoy it. Most parents buy a walker under the assumption that it will let them kill two birds with one stone: entertain baby and let mom/dad do housework. If you plan to turn your attention elsewhere, a walker is an accident waiting to happen. Gates can be knocked over or unseen obstacles may tip it over. If you intend to play with the baby, you don't need the walker.

The injuries that can be sustained from walkers include serious head injuries, neck fractures, and leg fractures. Typically, distraught parents report that they were momentarily distracted, or that they had *no* idea that the baby was so close to the stairs, or that they didn't know he could even get there.

A perfectly acceptable alternative is a walker minus wheels. These usually bounce or spin in place. The idea is the same: Place the child in a seat he can bounce up and down in, complete with a tabletop for toys. Your baby will never know that he's missing out on his first set of wheels, and you'll never miss the eight-hour wait at your local ER.

TIP

The baby who wouldn't sleep

S ome babies need to be left to cry themselves to sleep. They expend their dwindling energies bit by bit, and the noisy, cranky cries gradually taper off to a whimper, then deep sleep-breathing. But not all babies.

If he gets increasingly wound up the more he cries, don't just put him to bed and tiptoe away. Stay with him. Pat him on his belly or back or sing softly to him. Keep on patting and gently murmuring to him until the intensity of his cries drops off and dies away. This may take a *long* time and is in distinct contrast to all the foregoing advice that he has to learn to sleep by himself, *sometime*. Well, this is just not the time for your baby.

TIP

215

Donut on the head

Sorry, I'm not authorizing a trip to Dunkin' Donuts. The kind of donuts you need for this are the rainbow-colored, stackable plastic rings that every baby seems to have. Take a large ring (purple is always large, yellow always seems to end up at the small end) and put it on her head when she's sitting. It will, of course, immediately slide off. Then place it back on again. Most of the time, babies appreciate this game and start to laugh. As she gets older and develops better eye-hand coordination, she will start reaching for the ring; and as she gets older still, she will actually be able to keep it balanced on her head for longer and longer periods.

The play yard: don'ts

There is a limit to the amount of relief a play yard provides. After about the age of six or seven months, your baby may take one look at the play yard and howl in protest. Even if he doesn't mind sitting in the play yard, *don't* use it to deprive him of your company for long stretches. While some placid babies accept whatever circumstances are thrown their way, even if the play yard is loaded up with all the latest toys, he still needs the stimulation that only another person can provide.

At this stage of the game, it is best to use the play yard (or crib) only as a last resort for older babies. If you have a mobile baby who needs supervision that you can't immediately supply—such as when you have to go to the bathroom, put out a stove fire, or hand your irritated husband a beer—put your baby in the gates and make sure he's safe, has an ample toy supply, and a straight line of sight to you.

TIP

217

The amazing flying baby

When your baby is old enough to have head control, that is the necessary neck and back strength to hold his head upright, it is safe to start him on what I call "flying lessons." Hold him horizontally at arm's length, facing out, and take him for a "flight" around the family room. Or bedroom. Provide gentle "turbulence" by jiggling him slightly as he goes.

Dads will have thought of this the moment he was born; moms will no doubt fear excessive roughhousing. The safest way to fly is to lay him on your forearms, your hands in his armpits—that way you can spread his arms out as wings. And then you're set for takeoff.

Safety tip: Don't do this near stairs and make sure the floor has no loose toys that you might trip over.

3–12 MONTHS: BABYHOOD

Ear infection, part 1

One of the most common health problems in children is middle ear infection. The outer ear ends at the eardrum. Behind that is the middle ear, a cul-de-sac for the mucous membranes at the back of the throat. It is directly continuous with the nasal passages, esophagus, and mouth. Behind the middle ear is the inner ear, a cavity sitting inside the skull that contains the nerve endings that send impulses to the brain and translate vibrations into "hearing."

A runny nose, a sore throat, or basically any minor upper respiratory infection can clog up the middle ear with mucus and is a perfect medium for bacteria to grow in, turning the thin secretions into thick, pasty pus. Yum.

Your baby cries from the painful ear pressure. A day or two before this, however, he will already have been cranky, developed a runny nose, and possibly fever, a cough, or a lack of appetite.

Your doctor will likely prescribe antibiotics and a pain/fever medicine such as Tylenol or ibuprofen (Motrin, Advil, etc.).

TIP

219

Ear infection, part 2

When babies have ear infections, they often pull at their ears and cry from the pain. A few things help the pain, and many things that you may be tempted to try *don't*. In particular, cleaning the wax out of the *outer* ear, the ear canal, does nothing to relieve the pressure and infection in the *middle* ear. Don't stick anything into your baby's ears smaller than your fingertip. That grungy, brown wax you see emerging from deep within may be the most offensive thing imaginable, but leave it alone. Normal baby earwax does not obstruct hearing, and it actually performs a valuable function (It protects against cooties). Your baby's ear only needs cleaning in the doctor's office, to rule out an infection. Most doctors use special "cerumen spoons" to remove the wax and allow visualization of the eardrum.

Putting a marginally protected stick into your baby's ear is asking for trouble. A sudden, swift head movement toward the stick could perforate the eardrum, disrupt the normal architecture of the three fine bones in the middle ear, and potentially cause permanent scarring and hearing problems.

TIP

Ear infection, part 3

It's been two days, and your baby's ear infection is still not obviously better. The crying and ear tugging continue, he may even have a fever, and his congestion is no better. What to do?

If you call your pediatrician after 8 P.M., you will either be sent to the ER or told to come into the office tomorrow. Meanwhile, you have the prospect of another sleepless night.

Apply a few drops of warmed (not hot) olive oil with an ear dropper into the ear. (Note: Always test it on yourself first). An old Greek woman suggested this to me during her granddaughter's office visit, and sure enough, two weeks later, the mother reported that it worked every time. This is not an officially-sanctioned treatment, it may not work, and it may get a little messy, but it may be what your baby needs.

TIP

Nursing refusal

A couple of causes may be at work if your baby, who up until now was a happy feeder, suddenly starts crying when you attempt to nurse her. Some things to consider:

- Teething. Painful gums may turn a choice part of his day into a torturous encounter.
- Sensitivity to your soap or scents.
- Impending viral syndrome with nasal stuffiness, fever, and upset stomach.
- Ear infection. The fluid in the ear may cause painful pressure on the eardrum when she gets into a horizontal position.
- Not ready to feed. If you have a baby who is on a strict schedule—yours—consider this a message that she's developed her own mealtime and playtime schedule.

TIP

222

Diapering when there's a rash

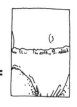

A diaper rash can be a source of protracted crying and overall crankiness. There are some easy pitfalls that you can avoid that make a bad situation worse.

Don't continue to apply occlusive creams or ointments like Vaseline or Desitin when your baby has a diaper rash. This locks in the germs or irritants along with the medicine you are applying, and your baby's skin needs as much air contact as possible. You can start it again after the rash is healed, but continued use may be one reason why a rash takes forever to heal. If your baby is getting over a bout of diarrhea that caused the rash, keep her bottom undiapered for brief—monitored—periods. This is the ultimate in air exposure. (Don't try this around anything but easily cleaned surfaces, like linoleum.)

Cornstarch is also okay to use—*except* when a yeast infection is present. The yeast, a living organism, consumes the cornstarch and the rash may spread explosively.

TIP

273

Baby blasts

A very gentle woman told me about this one. She holds her baby in a sort of football hold, crooked in her arm, face down. "Baby ready for blast off?" she asks and nods. Then she goes "tchk, tchk, tchk," slowly ratcheting the baby upward and outward a couple of inches at a time until he's at shoulder height. Then, with a "Whee!" she lifts him up and does a sort of pirouette.

Her son loves it, a fact to which I can personally attest.

TIP

224

Ruining a good night's sleep

When your baby wakes up crying in the middle of the night in the first few months of life, he's either hungry or has a messy diaper. He *needs* attention. When he wakes up in the wee hours after that, he has become accustomed to being fed or changed. The difference between what he *needs* and what he *wants* is enormous and you will grapple with it for the rest of your parenting days.

Once you have established that there are no *needs* to be attended to, it's okay to let your baby cry himself to sleep. There are many ways to accomplish this, and all are based on a gradual withdrawal of comforting methods.

- Nurse/feed him for shorter periods.
- Stretch out the interval between feedings.
- Wait a few minutes before feeding. Sing a song or pat him rhythmically.
- Dilute the formula gradually, or offer water instead.

TIP

Just say no: sugar water

If you know your baby readily calms himself down by sucking, but a pacifier isn't working, try giving him a bottle of water instead. Water is nature's perfect beverage.

Don't add sugar. Babies do not need the extra calories nor do they need to get into the habit of consuming only sweetened drinks. That is a habit they could have and regret for a lifetime. If he needs to feed, give him formula. If he ate an hour ago and you know he wants to suck on something, give two or three ounces of plain water rather than a pacifier. There is no such thing as drinking too much water. And if he takes the whole bottle, it may be that he *is* hungry.

TIP

Performance art

Don't give in to crocodile tears. She may be capable of turning on the waterworks to rival the death scene from *Camille*. The typical situation goes like this: Baby is happily playing with dad or the baby-sitter. Mommy comes home and all of a sudden, the mouth drops into a dead pout, the chin quivers, and baby does the stuttering *hu- hu- hu-* breathing that turns into a raucous, pained cry.

Don't let her get away with it. It is an early form of manipulation, pure and simple, to attain that ultimate in security objects, mama. Even at six or seven months, when you are likely to see such behavior for the first time, it is possible to coax her out of it. Give her lots of hugs or snuggles (dad or the baby-sitter, that is), with mom at arm's length, tell her that she's okay, that mommy is right here, and then, when she learns to settle down, reward her with a visit to mommy.

Although this may not teach her much about patience, it is a good practice run for the more taxing disciplinary challenges that lie ahead.

Watch the honey, honey

I've often heard new moms ask if honey is good for crying, since it sweetens the formula for a hungry baby. Often, they admit that *their* moms are pressuring them to try it.

Never flavor your baby's food with honey. Honey is no more nutritionally vital to your baby than cigarettes or plain sugar (Julie Andrews, forgive me, but a spoonful of sugar does *not* make the medicine go down).

Besides that, there is a very real health risk to babies. Honey (as well as corn syrup) may contain spores of the bacterial species *Clostridium botulinum*. These spores colonize the intestinal tract and release a neurotoxin that causes progressive lethargy, severe dehydration, and weakness. It may progress to paralysis and pneumonia, and can rarely be fatal.

Infants older than a year are immune to this, presumably because their stomach acids are strong enough to destroy the botulism spores.

Weaning

Weaning him from the breast is sure to cause crying. The time may come, though, when you have to give up nursing. Your baby will be more amenable to weaning if you wean him young—at about three months. Just as giving up a pacifier is relatively easy at this age because *all* experiences are new enough, switching to a bottle here is easier than it will be at six or eight months. (Note: The AAP recommends breastfeeding for at least six months and ideally one year.)

Some babies may reject weaning because of the taste of formula. For those babies, the transition will be easier if you express and bottle your milk for at least the first week so that he gets used to the new arrangement and new nipple. The next week, add a gradually rising proportion of formula so the change in taste is less noticeable.

Your baby may just take to the change more readily than you will, especially if you had a battle to get him to take to the breast in the first place. This is a poignant moment, to be sure; however, if you are intent on breastfeeding, have another baby.

TIP

Telecommuting

Who knows best how to manage your baby's inconsolable crying? You do, of course. Who knows best the insurmountable obstacles to being a successful supermom? You do. Who would rather stay home with your baby? You would.

So why leave the house to work? If your work can be done at home, why not become a telecommuter like millions of others? Then, you can be home to calm your baby's worst moments. Telecommuting is easiest if your job is measured by *output* rather than hours logged. Establish a regular means of communicating with your boss/office, meet your goals, and *voila*! Supermom—taking care of baby and taking care of business!

More and more companies are employing folks in this way. Take advantage of prior policies or precedents, if there are any. Remind them that you are saving office and parking space. With time, you'll find the right balance of home and office as baby grows and becomes more independent.

TIP

(It's likely that you'll need someone to help you take care of baby at least part of the day if you expect to get anything done.)

The disadvantage of working at home: cabin fever.

230

Food rejection, part 1

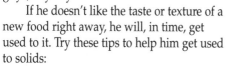

Starting your baby on solid food is, as Mark Twain once said about second marriages, the triumph of faith over experience. Look at it from your baby's point of view: First he was in a nice cozy room for months and months, then he was evicted into a cold, hostile environment. He's finally gotten used to certain, dependable facts of life: He can sleep in whenever he wants, he gets changed whenever he needs it, and when he's hungry, a nice breast or bottle is always available. So why are you trying to get him to eat something else? What is it with you guys, anyway?

If he doesn't like the taste or texture of a new food right away, he will, in time, get used to it. Try these tips to help him get used to solids:

- Feed him on an empty tummy. You or I would eat cod liver oil if we were hungry enough, and your baby may overcome his dislike for solid food if *he* is hungry enough.
- Also, avoid pushing the spoon too far into his mouth.
- Check the diaper before the meal.

TIP

Food rejection, part 2

If you've tried all of the foregoing and he still cries and pushes away food every time you try it, there are still a few more tricks up your sleeve:

- Make sure he is sitting comfortably. However, putting him on your lap (or someone else's) is probably a bad idea unless you like partially digested baby cereal all over your clothes. If he is too small to sit in a highchair, try feeding him in his car seat or in a bouncy seat. *Never* feed him in a reclining position.
- Some babies have a particularly strong need to suck and will be upset if they can't suck their meal. For these babies, offer just an ounce or two of breastmilk or formula, then progress to solids.
- Have a backup meal ready. This may mean nursing him or going back to plain old formula. No big deal, he'll get his calories either way. As time goes on, he will gradually get more and more calories from solids.

TIP

The daily news

Read your baby the newspaper. Seriously. Make a big production out of it. A smallish paper like the New York *Daily News* is ideal because it has lots of pictures and the pages are small enough to hold without your arms flailing all over the place. (The *Wall Street Journal* is a little dry for this purpose, but the *Weekly World News* or other tabloids are ideal.)

Use a deep, newsreel-type voice and invent wildly from the headlines, liberally sprinkling in words and phrases that are meaningful to your baby. "UN inspectors find evidence of Iraqi weapons" can become "Baby inspectors find evidence of diaper poopies!" Then rattle the pages noisily to open the paper. Lower your voice as you read the story: "Baby booboo woke up from his nap today with a poopie the size of Tehran. CNN first reported the incident after local nose sensors detected the signature smell-wavelength …"

By the age of ten or eleven months, when babies love nothing more than to tear paper, this is an ideal diversion.

TIP

233

(C'mon baby, let's do) the twist

Babies love to be gently swung around and around in a circle. This is a law of nature, perhaps the same one that tells dogs to chase their tails. You can certainly pirouette on one foot while holding baby to your heart's content, or you can get into an office chair or a bar stool and spin around just like you did when you were a child.

Don't have one? If your stroller has freely moving front and back wheels, you can use that to spin baby in circles (slowly, gently).

The Precautions: Make sure that baby is strapped in, has not fed recently, and no disapproving grandparents or neighbors are nearby.

Teething, part 3

Benzocaine (Orajel®, Anbesol®) is a local anesthetic, like lidocaine, that is widely used for teething. It is applied directly to the gums and should provide all of about ten minutes of relief. This doesn't sound like a big deal, but it does buy you a short period of time during which your poor, unhappy baby might be comfortable enough to nurse, eat a meal, or drink a bottle—which he might not do when his gums are sore.

When parents complain that a remedy doesn't work, as frequently happens with benzocaine, I often point out that a given remedy may only have a specific, limited role. For those times when you don't want or need to feed her, try some of the other teething methods above.

TIP

235

Just say no: sleeping with a bottle

A common practice that you should avoid is leaving your tired, fussy baby alone in his crib, drinking from a bottle until he's asleep. If your baby is hungry, make sure he's well fed before putting him down for a nap or for the night. Once he's tired (and crying) but well fed, don't resort to the bottle.

The juice or milk that pools in his mouth could spill into the ear canal, leading to ear infections. The constant pressure of the bottle against his gums could cause rapid tooth destruction, which, if severe, could even affect the permanent teeth. For this reason, putting a baby to bed with a pacifier is even an iffy thing to do. If he can *only* get to sleep by sucking on a pacifier, be sure to take it out once he's asleep, and try to come up with a new beddy-bye routine that doesn't include the pacifier as soon as possible.

TIP

236

Setting limits

A round about the eighth or ninth month, when baby is experiencing the joys of mobility for the first time, she is also experiencing discipline for the first time. "No" is something she may hear a lot. Some babies handle this better than others, but a sensitive baby can dissolve into tears each time mom raises her voice to say "no."

Setting limits is one of the tough jobs of parenting, but it can't be helped. She needs to learn not to touch the stove or the sleeping dog. But you don't want to be a meany, either. Say "no" *gently* when she heads toward a danger, and redirect her if necessary. When she gets older, you will be able to explain *why* you don't want her to do something, but setting limits gently but firmly will do for now. You may also be able to childproof one room so thoroughly that you avoid having to curtail her activities all the time.

TIP

237

Older sibs

If you have an older child, then you have another resource to combat crying. If your baby is fussy or just bored, he may enjoy some cheering up from his older sibling.

Older children often are sympathetic to crying babies as much as their parents, and they often spontaneously offer toys, make faces, or play games to try to comfort them.

But use an appropriate level of caution…toddler-age older siblings make lousy baby-sitters. Never leave your baby unattended with an older child until he is old enough to understand how to care for a baby. A four-year-old may take away baby's toys, may inadvertently give him a toy that he could choke on, or do something else equally dangerous, such as picking him up and dropping him. Sibling rivalry is also a consideration. You don't want to come in and find your three-year-old standing on the head of your three-month-old.

TIP

238

Bring dad into the loop

Has dad fallen into the role of best supporting actor? When baby won't calm down right away, does he act as if the *only* way to calm him is to give him back to mom? I'm sure there are many dads out there who expect this book to go something like this:

1. Give him to mom.
2. Give him to mom.
3. Give him to mom.
363. Give her to mom.
364. Give her to mom.
365. Give her to mom.

If dad is unsure of his parenting skills, tune in more carefully to what mom does. She has successful routines for feeding, changing, holding and singing to him, and dad should try to mimic them—especially those things she does when baby won't immediately calm down.

Don't give up. A persistent dad will get the hang of it and discover for *himself* what works and what doesn't work. In time, you may find dad has some special trick that mom cannot replicate.

Then you'll really feel like a dad.

TIP

Taking medicine

Giving a baby medicine does not have to mean that you will make your baby cry.

There are many medicine-taking techniques, and some babies respond to them better than others. I have seen babies who gulp down the pink stuff as well as those who need a full, four-point restraint, plus a head hold. This latter type can't be fooled by the old meds-in-the-applesauce routine. To optimize the experience, try these tricks:

- Refrigerate or chill it in the freezer to cut the taste.
- Avoid medication that you know has a bad taste. Some are notoriously bad-tasting, and most have some viable alternative.
- Avoid cold-and-cough medicines that don't really work anyway. Why ask for trouble?
- Combine meds (if okayed by your pharmacist) if more than one are needed.
- Ask for medication that can be given once or twice a day instead of three or four times.
- *Never* administer medications that are left over from last time (like giving old antibiotics for what you *think* may be an ear infection, before you actually get to the doctor).

Croup

Croup is a viral illness that has the most distinctive cough in all of medicine: It sounds like a barking seal. The progression of illness is also quite distinctive: an abrupt onset of high fever (103°F to 105°F), the barking, painful cough, and sometimes shortness of breath due to the cough's intensity. Croup almost always starts at night and then lasts for three nights. Daytime is usually calmer for a baby with croup.

To manage coughing, start by placing a humidifier at baby's cribside (which may prevent a bad cough altogether). Once a coughing bout begins, bring the baby into the bathroom, turn on the hot water in the shower, close the door, and allow the room to fill with mist. If this doesn't help her, get in the car and drive. The cooler, drier night air often helps (or maybe the cough just wears itself out after a while). Why cool and dry air following warm and moist air helps the croup has always baffled me. In spring and fall, the prime croup seasons, a smiling, happy 1:00 A.M. croupy kid is almost a nightly event in the ER. The parents generally tell me they tried the shower trick and then the car ride, and by the time they got to the ER, things were looking better.

Antibiotics do not help croup since it is a viral infection.

TIP

Mouth sores

Among the myriad viruses that afflict babies, none is more likely to make them more miserable than the ones that cause mouth sores. These are small, faint blisters that appear singly or in crops along the lips, gums, tongue, or back along the tonsils. They last anywhere from three to seven cranky days.

Although a doctor can often readily distinguish between viral blisters and the pus that appears at the back of the throat with a strep infection, the differences may not be as readily apparent to parents. If you think your baby might have strep, call your doctor. Keep in mind, though, that strep (which requires antibiotic treatment) is exceedingly rare in children under about eighteen months. Viral throat infections are much more common, and they go away without prescription medication.

What you can do to make baby more comfortable:

- Give her ice pops to suck on.
- Apply benzocaine (Anbesol, Orajel, etc.) to the sores before meals or drinking.
- Mix equal amounts of Kaopectate and Benadryl solutions, give a half to one teaspoon three or four times a day (before meals). This acts as a local anesthetic.

Cellulitis

Cellulitis is a bacterial infection of the skin. Bacteria enter the bloodstream in two ways: through a break in the skin or from the mouth and nose, where they usually reside harmlessly. Once inside the bloodstream, they may settle into a particular site and begin to grow, causing a localized infection. This is characterized by a diffuse redness, swelling, warmth, and localized tenderness. Fever and irritability are common but not universal.

If you think your baby has cellulitis or are not sure, call your doctor or go to the ER. This is a situation that requires antibiotics, occasionally given through an IV or as an intramuscular (IM) shot.

TIP

Burns

Burns become a risk in the second half of baby's first year. There are two kinds of common splash burns: those from containers of hot water and those from turning on the tap.

In order to prevent hot coffee or tea splashes, avoid carrying the baby around when you're drinking your Starbucks®. Once baby starts crawling and climbing, keep the coffee and tea mugs away from the edges of tables, and keep the handles of cooking pots turned in toward the stove top.

To prevent tap water burns, turn the thermostat on your hot water heater down from 165°F, a typical setting, to 120°F to 125°F, which is much less likely to cause burns on contact. If you have a water cooler at home, put a lock over the hot water dispenser, which babies may inadvertently push open while climbing or exploring.

TIP

244

Bone or joint infections

Crying that accompanies fever and a limp should receive immediate medical attention. Most of the time the cause is benign, but a few conditions need to be considered.

Infection of the bone (osteomyelitis) or joints (septic arthritis) are fortunately quite rare in infants. In either disorder, baby will have a fever, often 103°F or greater, and pain on using the affecting limb. Since the knee or hip usually are affected, the pain is evident when your baby tries to stand or otherwise bear weight. There may or may not be swelling, but the bone or joint pain should be obvious enough.

Both conditions require some diagnostic tests and are treated with IV antibiotics. Septic arthritis generally requires surgery to drain the inflammation from the affected joint. However, with prompt and thorough treatment, long-term consequences are minimal.

TIP

Swollen lymph nodes

Swollen lymph nodes may cause crying due either to pain or to irritation. The lymph nodes (they are not *glands*, as they do not secrete anything) in the neck often become mildly enlarged with an upper respiratory infection. There are two main chains, one on each side of the muscle that runs diagonally from behind the ear to the tip of the clavicle that sits on top of the breastbone. The anterior (front) chain is the one that gets enlarged more commonly than the posterior (back) chain, but both may pop up with an infection.

Enlargement of these nodes during a minor illness is a sign that they are producing antibodies and lymphocytes, which are the means by which your baby *gets over* a cold. Occasionally, the lymph node itself becomes infected. That is, the germs that are being digested within the lymph node may occasionally overwhelm the artillery being brought against them. Then the node itself becomes infected, a condition known as cervical adenitis.

When an affected node becomes larger and more painful than the others, your baby may show pain on moving the head from side to side because the muscle may go into mild spasm. This is a minor condition that requires antibiotics but in no way represents a serious illness.

TIP

246

Intussusception

A very peculiar condition known as intussusception may arise in the second half of the first year. This is a situation where the intestine folds into itself, much like a telescope folds into a cylinder. The symptoms are subtle but characteristic: A bout of crying, where baby appears to have painful abdominal cramps, is followed by a period of complete calm and comfort. There is vomiting, but no diarrhea. This may go on for hours before the pattern becomes clear. At some point, usually later on, the baby may pass a bowel movement that looks dark red and mucusy like currant jelly.

This is a situation that should be treated in the ER because a barium enema is necessary to push the bowel back in the right place. Following that, the baby should be fine, but he will need a night in the hospital to recover.

TIP

247

Toxic synovitis

Crying with a limp and no or *low* fever may turn out to be toxic synovitis.

Despite its ominous name, toxic synovitis is a relatively benign childhood condition. It is a mild inflammation of the hip joint characterized by a moderately painful limp, crying when the child walks, and a low-grade fever. It usually lasts for only a few days. It may follow a viral infection. The pain of standing on the affected leg may stop some toddlers from walking altogether.

This condition is often difficult to diagnose because it often does not have visual cues like swelling. In the ER, an evaluation includes X-rays and blood tests to look for more serious kinds of bone or joint infection. It is sometimes necessary to hospitalize such children if there is any chance that one of these infections is present.

Toxic synovitis warrants watching at home, but it will get better in a few days. Provide Tylenol or ibuprofen for comfort, and check again with your doctor if the condition worsens.

TIP

248

12-24 MONTHS:
TODDLERHOOD

Exploration

Sometimes it's okay to let a toddler get into a situation where you know he might cry. All children need to experiment with their world, their parents, and their own limits. As he learns to walk, you sometimes have to let him fall over bumps in order for him to understand the concept of going around obstacles. Let him find out that if he turns the knobs on the stereo, he is in for a loud blast in his ear.

Keep an eye on his environment to make sure that he's safe. Don't, for example, let him discover a hot oven door firsthand, don't let him yank on a dog's tail, but don't put him in a bubble, either. As he discovers some facts of life on his own, he learns for himself what safety is all about. And he also won't be afraid of new situations when he's older.

When he does fall and scrape himself, let him know that he's all right. Don't lose your head, and he'll learn not to lose his.

TIP

249

Under cover

An important variation on the peekaboo game—important in the sense that it provides ample play opportunity—is the hiding-in-the-sheets game. This works nicely when you are trying to wean him. Let's say that you want to break him of his wake-up-and-nurse routine. Bring him into bed and throw the covers over him, calling out "Where's baby? Where's baby!??" This may distract him enough to let him take a bottle instead of *you*.

If your baby cries at being thrown into darkness, throw the sheets over your own head for the first few times, until he gets the hang of the game. Then, when he's amenable to being covered up himself, you can throw in the bottle while he's playing.

Older babies and toddlers love this game and will tolerate you throwing their favorite blankie on their head even if they would not otherwise let it out of their clutches. A final twist: Cover up both you and your baby's head and "hide" from the world.

TIP

250

Sticker chart

If your kid is mature enough, and by eighteen months many children are, you can negotiate her out of a tantrum by something as simple as a star chart. Reward an hour of good behavior with a shiny sticker on a flashy chart. For example, when she begins to start whining, yelling, or throwing things, hold up the chart to her and tell her that she is due for a new sticker in five minutes, if she'll stop misbehaving.

Early on, just the sticker can be reward enough. You'll soon discover that she'd rather plaster her shirt with stickers than waste it on a crummy piece of paper. In time, as she wises up to your methods, you'll have to rework the bargain to include a trade-in. That is, once she earns ten or fifteen stickers, she gets a reward—watch a video, a special dessert, etc.

TIP

Headphones

Headphones are a surprise the first time your child puts them on. Play him a favorite tape or a disc, with his own magical device on his head, and his attitude should come around *toot sweet*.

After the first one or two tries at home, headphones should be considered mainly as a fundamental for long car trips. Crayons and sticker books and look-out-the-window games can only entertain for so long; unless you can tolerate kid songs for long stretches of time, a personal stereo is the ideal solution. And, when older sibs protest that they don't want to hear their baby sister's tapes, bring along a set for them as well.

TIP

252

Going somewhere?

On a rainy, rainy day, after you've painted and puzzled, napped and snacked, the borings settle in. Go for a bus ride in your own kitchen. Have your toddler, who's crying because he's just busted up the puzzle he worked at all morning, line up all the kitchen chairs, and then make him the driver. Tell him that you need to go to the museum and then you want to go to the movies. Give him a Frisbee for a steering wheel. Call out the sights along the way, make him stop for other passengers (throwing his favorite stuffed animals on board). Sing "The Wheels on the Bus" and complain about the bumps.

Get sneaky: Call for Chinese food to be delivered, and then when it arrives, pretend you've gone for takeout. After all, on *that* kind of a day, who wants to cook?

TIP

Finger guy

It starts with Eeny-Meeny-Miney-Mo. Then your finger starts tapping baby's nose, chin, ears. Finger guy is clearly out of control! "Excuse me, Finger guy," you say as you look your fingertip in the face. "You were doing it all wrong. It goes from potato to potato, not all over the place! "Then curl your finger up, just like a two year old who's just made a mess. "Do you promise to behave? "Finger guy nods briskly. "OK, then let's try it again."

Give Finger guy a couple of chances, and make sure he messes up each time. Older children will fall into paroxysms of laughter (one time Finger guy even razzed me while my boys were in the tub! They never forgot Finger guy after that), but even young toddlers get the idea of the game very quickly.

TIP

254

Baby videos

If you're like most new parents, when you had your first baby you bought your first camcorder. Every moment of your baby's first few weeks was recorded for all eternity. Then as the months went by, you slacked off a little. Then it was a rare moment here and there for something special like a birthday party or a holiday.

By the time the second baby arrived, it gathered dust for weeks at a time, and an event like baby's first steps went unrecorded and lost. Third babies are lucky if they have even a still picture now and then.

Your video library of those first few weeks can be quite helpful long before they become fodder for their wedding or Bar Mitzvah video. When you've got a bored and cranky toddler, show him a tape of when he was a baby, and relive his first few milestones with him. Toddlers love videos, especially when they, themselves, are the star.

TIP

255

Soup

Even picky eaters love soup. Even when our daughter Zoe briskly flung away each and every spoonful of baby food, with a finality that usually is only seen by corporate bosses, she would always consent to a spoonful of soup.

That paves the way for the soup game. If you have plastic tableware—plates, bowls, forks, spoons—try feeding your baby pretend soup when she's crying. Take a few mouthfuls first, with an exaggerated "Oooh! Yummy! Gorilla soup! All for me!" Then offer her a mouthful. If she's still crying, take it away at the last second, as it's poised in front of her, and then she'll *really* get mad. The next time she can have her soup, and at that point she's playing the game. You win. (Optional points are scored for hopping around and scratching yourself like a gorilla.)

TIP

256

Round two goes to baby!

As the parent, you win plenty of battles. Keep your eyes and ears open for opportunities when your child can successfully plea—or cry—his case. He doesn't always want to share a toy with a sibling or a playmate, and he won't always want to wear the outfit you've picked for him. Every now and then, let him taste success (independence!) by letting him decide for himself when he shares a toy or what outfit he wears.

Letting him make his own choices can backfire, however, if you offer too many choices. He may become even more confused and escalate from tears to full-blown tantrum. So until he becomes a little older, give him a range of options a couple of times a day—and take charge the rest of the time.

TIP

The crying playmate

What do you do when you are in charge of someone else's toddler and she starts to cry? That depends on why she's crying.

It stands to reason that the same things that make your eighteen-month-old cry will make another toddler cry as well. The hungry, wet, bored, and oops-I've-just-bonked-myself cries pose no problem, but what do you do when she's throwing a tantrum or misbehaving? The answer lies in what the child expects to happen when she does this at home and what her parents do under these circumstances. The same disciplining, limit-setting, and time-out rules should apply to another toddler just as much as they do to yours. It will serve a visiting child poorly to know that she can go to a friend's house and have her misbehavior indulged in a way that wouldn't be at her own home. Furthermore, you won't want your own child to see that two sets of rules apply in her own house.

Before taking on the responsibility of another child, it always pays to go over the ground rules with the parent who is leaving the child. This way, you don't have to second guess appropriate rule setting.

TIP

258

Whining

Whining, like a tantrum, is just another means your toddler employs to get you to help her out or intervene in a crisis. Many parents who can handle cries, screams, and tantrums just can't handle the *whining*. It is the one thing that finally pushes them over the edge, and they give in to her request for a video, a snack—whatever.

Unfortunately for you, the whining may just be a simple message that she wants you to put down what you are doing and pay attention to her. If so, you have only a few choices:

- Play with her.
- Feed her or give her a drink if it's been awhile.
- If she can talk, respond by saying "Use your words. Whining hurts my ears."
- Don't call her a whiner.
- Don't yell at or punish her for it, either.

As with any undesired behavior, identify its cause, choose a behavior-modification program, and stick to it.

TIP

259

Privacy

In a dramatic contrast to the tears shed over being separated from mommy, there will be times when you run across your toddler engaged in some private activity (usually the first few times he will be pooping), and he will cry because he wants to be left alone. (This is truly the other side of the separation-anxiety coin.) He will pick out, in his own mind, those moments when he feels safe and controlled enough to enjoy a few private moments. At first, those moments will be limited to performing a bodily function or playing with a favorite toy. In time, he will want privacy during other activities as well.

As a baby, he may not have needed *any* time alone, but as he masters his environment, this will change. It is part of the transition from dependence to a fledgling sense of independence. As with any complex emotional task, it will take time for him to sort out his feelings. So for the time being, a little understanding on your part is all that is needed, and don't intrude when he cries to be left alone.

TIP

A night-light alternative

Is your bedtime ritual a twelve-step program? Do you get exhausted just trying to get your little girl into the *vicinity* of the bed? Did you spend weeks coaxing her to accept a night-light as a reason to stay in bed? And how many times does she pop up demanding water?

For those toddlers who wail at the mention of going to bed and fiercely dig their little paws in for a standoff, here's a new approach: glow-in-the-dark wall stickers. You'll find stars and planets, bugs, planes, just about any theme. Make it a game—let her pick which ones to put up when she goes to bed. Let her "wish upon a star." Do magic tricks to reveal them to her one by one.

For the first week or two, or until the novelty wears off, you probably won't be able to get her in bed soon enough.

TIP

261

The way the cookie crumbles

Food frustration is a common cause of the abrupt-crying-spell syndrome. Raise your hand if you've seen this one: He has paroxysms of grief when a cookie breaks or a sandwich is cut in the wrong direction. In our house, it usually was a signal that our son was tired and in need of a nap. If fatigue is not the issue, then he's probably expressing frustration at his lack of control over yet one more element in his environment. Assuming you wouldn't do anything so heartless as to give him a cookie that was already broken, try to get him to eat the broken cookie, the misshapen sandwich. This teaches one of two lessons:

- It tastes just as good whole or broken (demonstrated in several studies performed at NIH and Stanford University).
- These things happen.

Don't get carried away yourself, don't get upset that *he's* upset over something trivial, and don't believe those magazines that tell you that it's cheating on your diet to eat cookie crumbs. Sure, the crumbs have calories, but they are more than burned up in the stress of the situation (demonstrated in several studies performed in our own kitchen).

TIP

Discipline

A toddler's tantrum is a hot-tempered fit. It is born of frustration, fatigue, inability to express feelings or control events, and more. Just as he cried as a young baby for a specific set of needs, which became clearer with time, the toddler's tantrums represent a whole new language for a whole new set of challenges. He is becoming independent. Now he cries from uncertainty at how to respond to this new, scary world.

To paraphrase T. Berry Brazelton, the way you discipline him in any *single* incident is not as important as being consistent on *each* occasion. Until your toddler understands limits, you will spend an awful lot of time saying the same "No!" over and over again. It's okay. It *is* for his own good. So keep in mind the following:

- Don't withhold love—withhold approval for the action.
- Don't criticize the child—criticize her action.
- Don't hold her to unrealistic expectations.
- Don't be inconsistent—the same rules apply all day, every day.
- Don't be surprised if it takes forever!

TIP

Enlist the help of friends—his friends!

Your toddler's best friends, his stuffed ones, that is, can be counted on as your allies to help win the battle against tears. They are willing to help in a number of ways.

- Have Moofie the Bear sit with him, saying "Don't be sad, baby." (It often helps to have a characteristic voice for each of his favorite pets.)
- Enlist your toddler's help in getting ReeRee the Kitty to stop crying: "Look! ReeRee is sad!
  Can you help her stop crying?"
- Have her break up a fight between Moofie and ReeRee.
- Let Moofie and ReeRee smother her in kisses.

Headache

Headache is uncommon in children under two. Children who do have headache usually cry. In order to identify headache as the cause of your child's tears, you will often need to point to each body part and ask if he is "sick" or "has a boo-boo" there.

The causes of headache are not often serious or worrisome in children this young. Most of the time a headache is due to a runny or stuffed-up nose, sinusitis, or an unwitnessed minor head trauma.

Children who are congested to the point of causing headache are best treated by using a cool mist humidifier or giving an antihistamine. Decongestants are rarely effective. On the other side of the coin, a child who has been given cough or cold medicine for more than a few days can develop "rebound" headaches from sudden withdrawal of the medication.

For kids who have hit their heads and have a mild headache, but no vomiting or excess sleepiness, all that is needed is acetaminophen or ibuprofen in the recommended amounts.

TIP

Rubber stamp kit

A great toy is flexible, multipurpose, and able to withstand a long afternoon with a kid who has played with it a thousand times before. A rubber stamp-art kit fits this description. The more stamps and ink colors it has, the better. Some have specific themes (dinosaurs, jungles, etc.), and some are all-purpose.

When your girl gets tired of stamping interesting pictures on her arms and clothes, start to write a stamp story. Make up names of characters. Retell fairy tales. Pretend the stamp creatures are mommy, daddy, brother, sister, and friends, and see what story your toddler creates.

It is a rare child who has played with a stamp kit so many times that they are really, thoroughly bored with one. Consider it a household staple.

TIP

266

Puzzles

Puzzles are good toys to have in an emergency. The first puzzles for toddlers are the wood inlay puzzles with a knob on each piece. Once she's tired from whatever activity she's doing, puzzles are always going to attract her attention. First, she can dump the pieces out (in a bad mood it's always nice to break something up). Then she can fit each piece back together, and by the time she's hunting for the right hole for each piece, she will have forgotten what was frustrating her in the first place. By age two they may even be ready for jigsaw puzzles.

And when the puzzle is done, dump it out and start all over again!

Paint

Prepare to get messy. When you've already done the crayon thing and the stamp thing, perhaps painting is the next direction to go. Most toy stores sell washable tempera paints either as markers or as tubes that can be squeezed out.

Make hand art. Squish your hand in the paint and make handprints. Then put your child's handprint next to yours. You've got an instant greeting card for when your spouse comes home from work. Or paint a dinosaur and give him human hands.

A little preparation is often needed. Either go to an established play area of the house or spread a lot of newspaper. Then throw on an old shirt for you and one of mom or dad's old shirts on your child to keep him (somewhat) clean.

Respect yourself

A tantrum is about as hard to tune out as a car alarm. But sometimes there's no better solution than turning a deaf ear. If he goes into hysterics over a torn book that stays torn no matter how many times he opens and shuts it, he may just be shrieking to test your limits. If you ignore his thunderstorm, he may learn that there is no point to being so unreasonable. By contrast, if you respond to each tremor, he will learn that he can impose his will above everyone else's just by turning up the decibels, and this is undesirable as well.

Tell him, when he's being beastly, that you have your own needs, and he can run his tantrum out in his own bedroom (or some other appropriately safe environment) and that you will respond when he is acting better. As with other tantrum-busters, it takes a certain amount of practice and self-assurance that you are correctly balancing your own needs against his. Once you feel comfortable with this, you should see and hear less of these out-of-control episodes.

TIP

269

Sore throat

A sore throat can cause tremendous pain and irritability. Viral throat infections are very common and can be nasty, but "strep" throat is the most common *bacterial* cause. Strep usually shows up as pain on swallowing and swollen tonsils, often with a layer of pus on top. Viral infections are milder but may look *exactly* like strep. Fever, cough, and poor appetite accompany both types of infection.

Since strep is not viral, it is treatable. Most, but not all doctors, take a throat culture before prescribing antibiotics. The reason to treat a strep throat with antibiotics is not as clear-cut as you might think: The infection, including the pain and fever, disappears in three to four days *even if you do nothing*. However, antibiotics do prevent the serious complications of acute rheumatic fever and glomerulonephritis.

Viral throat infections commonly improve by themselves without help. And, by taking antibiotics unnecessarily, there is a risk of adding to the serious problem of selecting resistant strains of bacteria. So the *best things* to do for a sore throat are the old-time remedies: hot soup, tea. If hot doesn't work, go cold and try ice pops.

TIP

A play group

Once you've completely exhausted all of the toys and games you can possibly play at home, and your toddler is still bored and cranky, think play group. If you don't already belong to one, this may be the time to start one. Children under two don't play socially yet. They engage in "parallel" rather than "cooperative" play. But most toddlers do gain some enjoyment from playing alongside other children.

Play groups also help create a circle of friends with whom they will play when they are ready. Some components of a successful play group are:

- Five to eight compatible children and parents.
- A regular time and home or park rotation.
- Ground rules (with the parents) for food and snacks.
- Ground rules (with the kids) for sharing toys or taking turns.
- Ground rules (with the parents) for arbitration resolution.

If your child doesn't take to a play group at first, give him time. All children mature at different rates, and he may take time to get adjusted.

TIP

271

Mom's little helper

Here's the question: Which is worse, the constant, whiny drone of a bored eighteen-month-old or the chaos of a kid in the kitchen? Easy. The whining. When you're cooking, you always need an extra pair of hands. With a toddler, that's just what you have.

In the beginning it is best not to give him any specific jobs to do; instead, give him a pot and a cup (preferably from *his own* cupboard) and he will happily "help" until his own culinary effort is done to perfection. He may even invent his own little project, and you can reinforce this creative play by asking to "try a taste of his soup."

The risk is mainly to your ears: Nothing deafens like the clatter of dropped pots and pans. In time, he can progress to being a full sous-chef and actually do an efficient job of beating eggs, tearing lettuce, and mixing batter. (Then you may be happy that you started him out in the kitchen so young!)

TIP

Constipation

Constipation in a toddler, unlike a baby, can be a major ordeal. After a day or two without pooping, children will often refuse to poop because they have hard stools that cause pain. After three or more days, a child will hide in a corner, rub his tummy, grit his teeth, and may even roll around on the floor crying miserably until the urge to "go" passes.

Constipation can occur in any child, especially one whose diet is high in processed carbohydrates (bread, spaghetti, etc.). Occasionally an episode of diarrhea causes a painful diaper rash, which starts the cycle of withholding stool. In many cases, however, it is a mystery as to why a child stops allowing himself to defecate. (Boys and girls are equally likely to suffer from this kind of constipation.)

Your doctor will most likely recommend enemas or suppositories followed by prune juice or mineral oil to keep his poops loose until he overcomes his fear of going to the bathroom. You can help your child stomach the mineral oil by mixing it with pudding or yogurt. Yum. You may need to stick with this regimen for a week or two until a normal, daily bowel movement routine returns again.

TIP

The library

Sometime deep in winter, both you and your baby will hit the great brick wall of total boredom. You will have done every puzzle a thousand times, watched every video, played every game, and still have a month before warm weather comes. You can no more tolerate her cries than you can spend another dollar at the mall on something *else* you don't need.

The answer: the library. It is a great play and learning resource for you and your child. It's a playground, a play group, and an educational center all in one, and it's *free*. There are music tapes, videos, CDs, and probably even software for you to check out that cost you nothing (unless you forget to return them).

If you are holding back because the word "library" conjures up images of endless hours of study, remember this: It's a new experience for your toddler, and one he'll want to repeat again and again. (And PS: If that's your only memories of the library, it serves you right for *not* making out in the stacks.)

TIP

274

The long and winding road

A baby who travels well does not necessarily become a toddler who travels well. Travel gets harder, not easier. Children get far more bored in far less time on the road.

The answer is: Bring lots and lots of stuff. A good rule of thumb is to pack one play item per half hour of travel for each kid. That is not to say that they can or will play with each item for half an hour, but it will give you a range and depth of options. Bring along a personal stereo for an older child if you don't if you don't think you can handle Barney songs for the entire length of the Florida panhandle. Stock up on sticker books. Toss in a travel table that has some deep pockets for crayons and paper.

If you're going to be on the road for over half an hour, make sure your child understands right away that this is a long trip. And forget about the dive-bomb trips you used to make when it was just you and your wife. Allow an extra fifteen to thirty minutes per hour, and use the time well. Make pit stops to get out and play (hide and seek, tag, red-light/green-light). You'll all need the break.

TIP

Beads in the ear

One characteristic that separates humans from other life forms is our ability to stuff a bead into our ears when we are about a year old. You certainly don't see ferrets doing this (and while I may be going out on a limb, I tend to think that we are more advanced than ferrets). There is no real point to asking baby "Why did you put that pea, toy, bead, button, pebble, toenail, etc., in your ear?" but since this is a story that you will retell again and again, you should be aware of your obligation as a storyteller to provide the cute response that he will tell you. Get it on videotape, if need be.

Oh. Sorry. Here's what to do about this:

Do *nothing* yourself (unless 90 percent of it is sticking out). Do *not* try to take it out. You will only push it in farther, cause more pain, and make it more difficult to remove. Go to the ER, or call your doctor. If it can be removed easily with office equipment, let your doctor do it. If it is buried deep and is firm, like an uncooked bean or a pebble, it may require sedation and removal by an ENT doctor.

TIP

276

Pebble in the nose

Only marginally less troublesome than a bead in the ear, but certainly as horrifying to discover, is the presence of a foreign body in baby's nose. A nasal foreign body may be less painful and may remain undetected for much longer, until there is a thick, copious discharge. If you are ever able to determine when it got there, the answer may be surprisingly long ago. As with ear deposits, when you try to find out *why* your little boo-boo put a kernel of popcorn up his nose, you may just get an endearing *I dunno-o-o*, but you may also get some funny, elaborate explanation.

Again, do nothing to remove it. Take your child to the doctor and let her remove it. Nostril objects are a little easier to remove because the nasal cavity is wider than the ear canal and is not surrounded by a narrow bony canal, like the deep end of the ear canal.

Oh, by the way, don't expect this to be a permanent lesson in not putting things where they don't belong. Many children are repeat offenders.

TIP

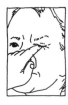

Dust motes in the eye

The eyes are just as susceptible to unwanted objects as are the nose and ears. The difference is that your child won't voluntarily put them there. A speck of dust or dirt may fly into your child's eye on a windy day or get scuffed up at the playground, sandbox, or beach. You may see it on the cornea or it may become lodged under the eyelid (usually the upper lid, since the lower one is too shallow). Occasionally, she may rub away the speck, leaving a corneal abrasion.

The first thing to do is irrigate the eye with lukewarm water, then go to the doctor or ER. Most airborne motes that land on the eye will stay there and continue to cause irritation until removed. They are easily removed with the help of anesthetic drops, and the eye will usually look and feel better in a day or two.

TIP

278

Turn the tables

Discipline should be consistent, but it need not be consistently dreary. If your child is getting into trouble, perhaps she needs company more than a toy. If she has just knocked over the flower pots you carefully planted (with *her*) yesterday, she is pushing your buttons. Maybe she wants to plant with you again.

Try this fun game. Grab her by the middle, turn her upside down, and say (a la Edward G. Robinson), "Naah! See, nobody knocks over *my* plants, see? Next time I'll plant *you* instead!" The downside of this is that she will make a game of knocking things over to encourage you to do it again.

Clinging

If there's one thing an independent-minded one-year-old wants, it's a little clinging time. You may have trouble even leaving the room. There she is, happily toddling around, pushing her shopping cart, but as soon as she sees your back, she'll cry for mommy. Then, when you turn to her again, she ignores you.

It may take her a little time to get used to the consequence of walking on her own: that once she walks away from mom, she's actually *away* from mom! This will pass in time, but until then, a little reassurance goes a long way. Keep her occupied with a "project" while you're in the next room or have your head turned. Ask her to "vacuum" the rug or to call her friends on her play telephone to set up a play date.

She will be more likely to cope well with small separations if you spend lots of good playtime with her.

TIP

Reschedule the toddler naptime

Sometime in the middle of the second year, your son will go from two naps a day to one. He will need about two hours of daytime sleep total, although children vary in their need for sleep. If he has just given up a morning nap, or is about to, he will probably get extra cranky at his normal naptime and then rally back. Ideally, you want him to take an early afternoon nap so that he has a good morning's worth of play, lunch, and then enough time to work up an appetite for dinner before going back to bed at a reasonable time.

Wind his activities down by 10:30 or 11:00 A.M. so that he has a chance to eat a peaceful lunch and then have a quiet time before napping. If, as our kids did, he insists that he's not napping, then have him at least lie down to rest after quiet time.

TIP

281

Herbal remedies

It is probably best to avoid herbal remedies for colds, aches, and minor injuries in older infants and toddlers. Herbal cures have not been shown to help resolve minor viral illnesses faster than the body will if left to itself. Nor is there a guarantee that herbs can help lessen the symptoms of illness, either. The AAP does not recommend herbal remedies, and the FDA does not regulate them as drugs. They are, instead, categorized as food products; and the FDA does not receive notices of adverse reactions to herbs the way they do for pharmaceuticals. Which means that you, as a parent, can only rely on their maker's claims about efficacy without scientific proof of benefits or documentation of risks.

As an aside, it is worth understanding the difference between homeopathic and herbal remedies. Herbal remedies are plant extracts in the form of a capsule, tea, or solution (often containing alcohol) with a high concentration of one or more active chemicals. Homeopathic remedies are highly diluted substances, essentially almost all water, that are supposed to provoke an immune reaction.

TIP

The irregular toddler

The irregular toddler, like the irregular baby, has difficulty keeping to a schedule and is inconsistent from one day to the next. Crying often comes from frustration with uncooperative toys, meals that never come at the right time, or the inability to establish a regular naptime. Once again, go with the flow or go against the grain. If you can, keep a diary or calendar to figure out things that calm him down and those that don't. Often, there is a subtle regularity to the chaos. On the other hand, some irregular toddlers can be steered toward a routine. The new skills of walking and talking may open up new avenues with which to impose some order on his day. A walk to the park in the morning followed by an early lunch and a nap may make at least half the day go by more smoothly.

The high-intensity toddler

The high-intensity toddler may not necessarily be a crier, but he can make *you* a crier. The powerful cries of infancy have been traded for the overactivity and high-decibel volume of a child who has the energy of a hockey team. The challenge is to find playmates and teachers who can cope with him. Don't let other parents and his teachers call him hyperactive. He's got more energy than the other children and needs to let it out constructively. He may have the same low tolerance for frustration as the others around him, but he's the one who lets you know first and loudest. Some remedies:

- Find playmates for him who can handle him, which may mean older children.
- Tell other parents about his activity level before you schedule a new play date.
- Make sure that teachers are savvy enough not to make this *your* problem by labeling him as hyperactive.
- Schedule plenty of playtime.
- Drink lots of coffee (yourself).

TIP

284

The negative toddler

A negative baby takes his serious disposition into his second year of life and keeps his wary frown ready for any new, suspect games or activities. A resource that may be helpful is a behavioral psychologist. A behavioral psychologist's focus is not the cause of the temperament or behavior. Instead, he or she will explore practical ways in which to sidetrack around an unwanted behavior to get to the desired one.

Depression and other mental illnesses are practically unheard of in children this young. The important exception is abused children, who experience a sudden change in personality, which is sometimes the only clue that an abusive situation exists.

TIP

285

The active toddler

The active toddler, like the high-intensity kid, burns both ends of your candle at once. Living with him is like living with the Energizer Bunny. He won't finish meals, splashes you incessantly at bathtime, and leaves any room a shambles after twenty minutes. He might, alas, have a lower threshold for throwing a tantrum or be prone to hurting other children and causing accidents. Slow him down, just like when he was a baby.

- Take him away from other kids or an activity if he is about to lose control.
- Bring along extra snacks when you go out—and forget about mealtimes.
- Redo your childproofing to eliminate climbing temptations.
- Plan activities that won't require him to sit still or quietly for long, or if you have to, plan ahead and make sure that you have an accessible "out" for him.

TIP

286

The sensitive toddler

Awareness of emotions and feelings of others—understanding that they exist at all—is an important developmental milestone for your child. It's the beginning of sensitivity.

The overly sensitive child cries easily. He does not tolerate frustration readily. He becomes discouraged at tasks that don't fall into place. He gives up and whimpers "not *work*ing!" He clings to your legs when you go to meet people or new places. He may get bullied easily.

Give him all the encouragement and rewards of success you can. If you catch him trying for the third time to master a toy or game, praise his persistence. If he cries, get him to tell you about his problem rather than cry. If you're in a bad mood, try to keep him from sensing it, as it might color his world negatively as well.

The guidelines for discipline and behavior that you apply for others should apply for him, as well. Just go gently.

TIP

Milk allergy, part 2

If you have made it through the first year exclusively breastfeeding your child and are ready to wean him, then a milk allergy may not appear until now. If so, the symptoms are likely to be the same as those seen in infants: irritability or crankiness, gas cramps, wheezing, runny nose, and itchy or eczematous skin.

If this describes what is happening to your child, discuss it with your doctor. Cow's milk is actually not as essential to your child's nutrition than you may be led to believe. Your child will thrive without it if he can not tolerate cow's milk for a few years. He can easily get his calcium, protein, and other needed nutrients from other food sources.

Coping with distractions

In case you've forgotten how to play like a toddler, it goes something like this: Become completely engrossed in the truck—doll—action figure—stuffed animal—play kitchen—pirate ship, make up characters who talk back and forth to each other, crash them into things (boys) or crash them into other things (girls), and then segue into a new scenario. However, there's no place in the script where mom or dad comes in and says "It's bathtime." Naturally, your attempts to limit their playtime will be met with wailing and screaming.

Play fair with your toddler. If he is so engaged in fantasy play that he can't be bothered, don't bother him if you don't really need to. If you are at another house and need to go home or if it's mealtime, try to head off a tantrum by giving a five-minute warning, then a two-minute warning, then gradually insinuating yourself into his play. Five minutes should allow him to wrap up the titanic events unfolding and move on to the next activity.

TIP

289

Climbing falls

Childproofing for a toddler is a different task than the first go-round for a crawler. Now, you have to consider that every object in her path may be turned into a stepping stone to the good stuff that you so recently placed "out of reach."

That concept no longer exists. *Everything* is "in reach," and you have to face that fact. Rather than trying to eliminate climbing, focus on eliminating the risks from falling. Delicate objects should be removed from your toddler's playroom, especially from bookcases. Numerous injuries and even some fatalities are sustained each year from toddlers pulling a freestanding bookcase or dresser on top of themselves. You can purchase special braces that allow you to bolt heavy pieces of furniture to the wall and thus eliminate this risk.

If she falls, don't overreact and don't panic. Assess the situation. If there is a serious injury, call for help and don't move her. If she seems to be okay, just reassure her that she is and then look around the room to see how you can prevent the event from occurring again: by removing the object she climbed on, the object she was climbing for, or her (from the room).

TIP

290

Whims

Toward the end of the second year, and often far beyond as well, your toddler may get whimsical notions in her head that you will be absolutely unable to derail—that she is, for example, Peter Pan and needs to wear a Peter Pan outfit. Offer a Snow White outfit instead and you are likely to be blown over by a tornado-force tantrum or drown in a sea of angry tears.

Some whims can be indulged more easily than others. It is probably easier for most parents to allow a little girl to be Peter Pan than it is to allow a young boy to go around as Alice in Wonderland. It is certainly easier to allow your toddler to wear a favorite sweatshirt in summer than to wear a bathing suit in February. On the other hand, some toddlers only learn the consequences of their actions firsthand. If you let him go out in the snow in a bathing suit, he will come back before long and never have *that* particular whim again. (He may, however, grow up and join the Polar Bear Club.)

TIP

Fears

Fearfulness is a natural response to an unfamiliar situation. This is as true for adults as it is for children, but a child's fears are easier to control. When a baby learns to walk for the first time, all sorts of new things are suddenly within reach, and she encounters different rooms and situations than she is used to. She may suddenly happen upon the dog's bed for the first time, startling *him*, too. The dog may bark suddenly, making her afraid to round that corner again.

Take her by the hand and walk right up to the doggie bed, chattering loudly so that the dog knows you are both coming, and you can be greeted by an excited lick or wag of the tail. If she gets frightened by this, too, steer her through it with a smile. She will smile too; if not this time, then next time. Soon she will take pride in understanding how she confronted this fear and overcame it. This is a useful tool to teach her for when she faces the next fear.

TIP

292

Poorly fitting shoes

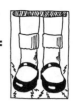

If the shoe fits, baby doesn't cry. If that new pair of WeeBoks causes WeeBooHoos, take 'em back. Any worthwhile store will exchange them; and this time around, try to figure out what went wrong in the process. Here are some shoe-buying tips:

- Don't take a cranky toddler for a shoe fitting.
- Make sure she's well fed and well rested.
- Go when you won't have to wait. Don't try shoes on a toddler who is bored from waiting.
- Test them yourself. If they feel to you like her feet have too much room or if they might pinch anywhere, don't buy them even if she has nothing to say about it.

TIP

Waking at night—again

During the course of a normal night's sleep, there are cycles of lighter and deeper sleep, as many as three or four cycles a night. In lighter stages of sleep, your little guy may wake up—and let you know it by crying. A loud, startled cry is worth checking out the first time it happens, but after a few nights of this, be wary of reinforcing the behavior. If he is normally a good sleeper and easy to put down for naps and bedtime, eliminating night wakings should be no problem. If he is a difficult kid in this regard, you can avoid warfare by using the same tactics for naps and bed: Minimize the rewards of waking, no food, no games, and stick to your game plan.

TIP

294

Night terrors

Night terrors are a phenomenon that occurs from twelve to twenty-four months of age. They are completely distinct from nightmares. A typical night terror episode often startles you from sleep and consists of screaming or crying and thrashing around. It may also be accompanied by sitting up, walking, or talking. An episode of night terrors generally occurs a few hours after falling asleep, and the child *remains asleep* throughout. The next day, the child recalls absolutely nothing.

By contrast, nightmares are milder, more familiar episodes of crying or fearfulness, often wake the child up, and are often recalled—vaguely. They generally take place toward the end of the night or early morning.

Since a night terror will not wake your child up, neither should you. You may want to consult with your doctor for peace of mind if nothing else.

Cuts

A cut needs stitches if the edges are gaping, if they can be gently pulled apart, or if fat is visible through the cut edges. (Fat looks like yellow popcorn kernels.) If you see fat, you will need to go to your doctor or the ER. (If you are going to the ER, make sure you know your child's immunization record.) Try to get there within six hours of the injury, as this significantly reduces the risk of the wound becoming infected. Sorry, the scar will be permanent.

Until you get there, use a damp, clean cloth to gently lift off dirt or debris. Once this is done, apply pressure with a fresh, clean cloth to stop the bleeding. Never put a tourniquet on, even if there is arterial bleeding (pumping blood), unless it cannot be stopped by pressure alone. A too-tight tourniquet can cause more damage than the cut itself.

TIP

296

Giving up the bottle

Not every child wants to give up the bottle. He knows the bottle, he likes the bottle, the bottle is his friend. And mister cup, you're no bottle!

A little attitude adjustment is called for—but understand his attitude first. If he clings to his last bottle at night, let that one alone. Give him a cup for dinner or snacking or when he is otherwise contented. Don't go looking for trouble by asking a whiny one-year-old to sacrifice one more thing.

Then go to step two. If he likes his juice from his bottle, offer him a choice: Drink the juice from a cup or keep the bottle and drink water instead.

Once he's down to one bottle a day, take a short break—without backsliding during the rest of the day—and in a week or so, offer a new, comfy bedtime ritual that doesn't include the bottle.

TIP

Molars

The first set of molars erupts sometime around ten to nineteen months and causes just as much misery as the first couple of teeth. In fact, more. They may wake him from sleep with their insistent pain (which is why it's always important to check out the situation when you hear a new or changed nocturnal cry), or they may just cause daytime anguish.

The same things should work as before: an iced teething ring, Tylenol or ibuprofen, or a topical anesthetic. Be cautious about offering other frozen foods that might present a choking hazard when they thaw out, especially since they are already placed in the back of the mouth.

TIP

I'm outa here!

Toddlers have been known to throw tantrums, complete with burning tears, soon after they are placed in their highchair for a family meal. What gives? Just like he knows the shape and color of his cup (or bottle), he knows exactly how much food goes or does not go into his little tummy. You probably have much less influence over his mealtimes than you may realize. His voracious appetite as a baby led you to believe that you pretty much were in control of things. I hate to break this to you, but you probably had just as little control then as now. Since his appetite has wound down and his selectivity has ratcheted up, you are the one who has to alter your expectations and strategies.

You may be able to trick him into staying at the table for one or two more mouthfuls by playing a variety of games or striking bargains. But when he's full, let him go. Complaining that he's eaten nothing will not increase his stomach's capacity. Rope him to the table and you'll get tears.

Don't worry. When he's hungry, as all of your and my ancestors have said, he'll eat!

TIP

Yelling

Yelling or screaming do not constitute "crying." They're worse. In the unlikely event that telling him to use an "indoor voice" works, read no further. However, most li'l yellers need a more interventionist approach.

- Speak in a whisper. If he wants to hear you, he will have to quiet down in order to hear you.
- Set up a special yelling time. Reward him for sticking to the time limit. Make sure it's a long enough time so that (if you can stand it) he tires out before the end. With enough repetitions, he may get tired of the yelling game.
- Redirect his energy into making animal noises. Chances are good that he will laugh himself into a quieter activity.
- Don't resort to screaming at him (unless you want to hear him roar "Shut up!" right back at you someday).

TIP

300

Separation anxiety

The end of the first year places your baby at a major turning point. In all likelihood, she can walk (or at least crawl), say a word or two words, and is, in general, ready to start being her own person.

It's a very frightening time, in case you've forgotten.

Nothing is more likely to provoke her deepest fears ("What if I'm not ready for this?") than the sight of mommy and daddy headed out the door. She may be ready to step into personhood, but not if you're not around!

The conniption that you witness as you step out the door is heart-wrenching but will likely disappear the moment you are out of earshot. It is her attempt to get you to change your mind and stick around a little while longer. You can weather this storm a little better if your child's caregiver spends a little time with you and baby before you are supposed to leave, to make for an easier transition (for the caregiver as much as the baby). If they can start to play together, it will make your departure carry less of an impact (although it is probably best not to just sneak out).

TIP

Crying instead of talking

Crying (or whimpering) is not only an annoying habit but may represent a strategy to overcome a minor deficit in expressive-language skills. Receptive skills, the ability to understand words and phrases, are reflected in the ability to follow one- or two-step commands ("Put down the toy" or "Stop kicking Jenny and come here now"). However, receptive language skills often far outpace *expressive* language skills, as reflected by his ability to point to his face, nose, etc., when you tell him to, but his inability to ask *you* to do the same with the same words.

A gap between expressive and receptive language functions is not necessarily a language delay, although if he is not speaking any words by eighteen months, you should discuss this with your doctor.

If he grunts or cries instead of saying what he means, work with him. Ask him if he wants the bread or the carrots, and don't accept pointing for an answer. Giving a verbal answer should get him the food *and* lavish praise.

Lead colic

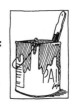

Lead poisoning is still around. The paint in many older homes is lead-based and poses a risk to toddlers, who eat paint chips or pick them up from the ground. Mild to moderate lead poisoning is generally asymptomatic, which is why doctors still screen for lead poisoning. At greater exposures children exhibit vague, intermittent abdominal pain that becomes more colicky with a large ingestion of lead. Vomiting and constipation may also occur. In cases of extreme exposure, symptoms include an altered level of consciousness, drowsiness, weakness, seizures, or coma. Long-term complications of lead poisoning include behavioral and learning disorders and seizures.

If you live in an old home or near a highway (fumes from gasoline may still contain some lead), contact your doctor. If your child does have lead poisoning, notify your local public health department or the Environmental Protection Agency (1-800-426-4791).

The best protection in a high-lead environment is good nutrition. If your child receives adequate iron and calcium, it is much more difficult for lead to enter into the circulation.

TIP

303

Crayons

It's time to scribble. Even though crayons are nontoxic (always check, anyway), you probably didn't let her play with them at a younger age when everything headed into her mouth. The first time you offer a bored, cranky toddler the chance to scribble on a piece of paper will undoubtedly prove a huge success as she realizes that she can fill the page with hundreds and thousands of swirls. Keep a close eye on her, though, or the table, walls, and furniture will soon have scribbles on them. That's when mommy and daddy are in for some big-time tears.

This is a good time to invest in an easel. It makes a great first birthday present, especially the kind that has a chalk board on one side and paper on the other side.

PS: Avoid pencils and pens, and any other sharp, pointy objects that could (yes, mom, I *promised* I'd put it in) put your eye out.

Dancing

If your child is crying from boredom, put on some kick-patootie rock 'n' roll and dance with him in your arms. Be sure to swing him around (gently!) as much as possible and (unless your child is built like and weighs as much as a fire hydrant) throw in a few dips as well. It may pay to have the music a *little* loud, so that when you sing along with the music, your child won't discover your lack of musical talent at so tender an age. In this way, I listened to Paul Simon's "Diamonds on the Soles of Her Shoes" roughly eight times a day for three or four months straight. When my second one came along, we boogied to Green Day. This method probably works with all genres of rock 'n' roll, reggae, hip-hop, rap, big band, doo-wop, and country/western. I suspect (but have not clinically tested this) that New Age music might not do the trick.

TIP

305

Battleground: the changing table

Crying, thrashing, kicking, and struggling when you change his diaper will probably become part of the routine sometime in the second year, if not before. It's just a phase, and sometimes there *is* a cause. Look to see if there is a rash that causes it to be an unpleasant experience or if the stool has a granitelike consistency. If so, some care or dietary changes might be in order. However, if the diaper is just a new place for the familiar war of independence, try a few new tactics of your own:

- Let him stand up for changes of diapers that are only wet.
- Let him undo the tapes and pull it down himself.
- Let him pick which diaper he wants to wear. They don't have to be different. Just offering a choice of three or so from the same pack may give him a sense of authority and control.
- Turn on a timer and announce that the diaper gets changed when the bell goes off.

TIP

306

Bug bites

Many bugs sting and cause minor itching. Some, like spiders and beetles, have painless bites but cause a skin reaction that becomes painful later on. Spider bites in particular tend to develop a large, tender area of redness with a central puncture mark, which can last for several days.

Bee, wasp, hornet, and fire ant stings are all painful immediately. These stings, unlike the others, may cause immediate allergic symptoms that extend beyond the site of the sting: hives, wheezing, nausea, vomiting, and swelling of the lips and tongue. If there is any question of respiratory symptoms (which does not include crying and low-level hysteria from the sting itself), call 911 immediately. If there are no symptoms beyond a red circle at the site of the sting itself, apply ice or a cold pack (taking care not to place the ice directly on the skin—frostbite has been known to occur from this).

TIP

Use reverse psychology

Reverse psychology can go a long way toward achieving some very important milestones: discipline, eating a meal peacefully, learning the notion of responsibility. At dinnertime, you may not be able to coax an eighteen-month-old into eating more chicken, but he may do it if you tell him not to: "This chicken is now *mine* and I don't want to see a single bite of it disappear!" Hold a forkful in front of his face, and his cries (or whines) will magically turn into a little sneaky smile and an empty fork. Follow-up is crucial: "Did you see who took my chicken? You help me track him down. I've got an idea! We'll leave a little chicken as bait, and you tell me when you see the thief!" Up goes the fork, down the hatch goes a little more chicken.

TIP

308

Trading places

When he's crying from frustration over a toy that won't cooperate, trade places, literally. You be the cranky toddler and make him the daddy. He will learn that it is not so easy to cope with crying, and you may be surprised to hear him repeating the same admonitions you have given him but thought he ignored.

My children used to pull my glasses off my face routinely and put them on their own faces. This started just as a play activity but became a useful tool once they recognized the role-reversal game. I also found out that if you listen to the messages they remember (and parrot back to you), it helps you to modify, soften, or vary the phrases you use.

Animal bites

Babies don't often get bitten by dogs or cats. Princess and Fido may feel disgruntled and displaced, but they respect the territory of the new arrival and expect the same consideration in return. That's why bites are only common after the baby becomes mobile. An exploring toddler or crawler may happen upon your dog's or cat's bed for the first time, like the comfy cushion, and climb into it, without realizing that he has just sent out a canine or feline nuclear alert. He certainly won't understand that Fifi's gentle nose-prodding is, in fact, a direct communication to get *OUT*, until it's too late.

If the animal involved is not the family pet, determine the animal's rabies vaccination status. If the animal is a stray, contact your local animal control office to try to capture the animal so that it can be tested (or, if you can do so safely, capture it yourself). Human rabies cases are exceedingly rare, but it is common in stray and wild animals. The AAP's 1997 guidelines for rabies treatment notes that bites of squirrels, hamsters, guinea pigs, gerbils, mice, rabbits, and hares almost never require antirabies treatment.

TIP

Security blankets and other objects

J ust as the moment of conception is often shrouded in mystery, it is often just as difficult to tell when a blanket or toy has been transformed into *the* favorite blanket or toy. That is, the object to which he is so firmly bonded that he will suffer loss of life or limb rather than part with his favorite "baki," "gigi," or "blanky."

These are called transitional objects because they are objects from which your toddler gains comfort as he makes the transition from dependent baby to independent child. He is transitioning from his dependence on you. So, just as he hates being separated from you when he's a baby, he would no more abide being separated from his *replacement* for you—the filthy, tattered, smelly blanket that was once, perhaps, a pretty baby present.

TIP

Good old Band-Aids

Never underestimate the power of a Band-Aid to heal the dreaded boo-boo. At the end of a long afternoon of jumping, throwing, and shrieking, there will invariably come a missed landing, an unseen step, a tripped-over toy. Even if there is no actual cut or scrape, the balm given by a brightly colored Band-Aid has no equal in medical science. Keep a supply handy, and you will never want for a quick fix.

Don't hold back slapping on a Band-Aid because you're afraid of the reaction that takes place when you pull it off, either. It need not be an exercise in patience (his or yours, as you try to get him to hold still while you give it a quick yank). Apply a small amount of lotion or Vaseline to the Band-Aid, and let it sit for a minute. This will moisten up the area and make the skin slippery.

TIP

Understanding tantrums, part 1

If you have a hard time understanding your little girl's tantrums, how do you think *she* feels about them? Put yourself in her shoes.

She has a number of complex emotions about difficult situations, which seem to come up hourly. When she gets into trouble with one particular activity –throwing cups, scribbling on the wall, yelling at baby sister—along comes mom and tells her to cut it out (along with a reminder that she has been told a million times before). It's hard for her to tell you that:

- Sometimes I can't tell when to be quiet.
- I was being creative—and you always like it when I'm creative.
- I was having fun and I wasn't hurting anybody!
- Why do we always have to do what *you* want to do?

Just try to remember that she would put a lot of things into words if she could. Until then, that's what your job is as a parent: Put her situations into words and explain them to her.

TIP

Understanding tantrums, part 2

Dr. T. Berry Brazelton defined crying as being a baby's first language. You might say that tantrums are a toddler's "language." Your baby's cries communicated his basic needs, first as simple as "I'm hungry," "wet," or "tired" cries. Then they expanded to include more subtle nuances such as "I'm overloaded," "Hold me," or "I'm afraid of that stranger." Now that your baby is a toddler and has learned the rudiments of spoken language, some of these needs can be expressed simply and easily, but there are still a bewildering variety of emotions and needs that are not easily expressed, except by crying, or, if you're unlucky, by hitting, yelling, throwing, or breaking.

Beyond that, your toddler is having a wholly new experience that he never encountered as a newborn: asserting his independence. Once he grasps the concept of himself as a person, he needs to assume control of himself and figure out how and when to be separate from mom and dad and when to stick close by. This is a complex task and will often cause him to throw up his hands in frustration—or pitch a royal fit.

TIP

Let them settle it for themselves

It may not seem as if there are enough hours in the day for your children to get into all the scrapes that they get into. Certainly it doesn't seem possible that they can fight over the same thing ("Mine!" "No it's MINE!") so many times each day. But there they are, at it again.

Child psychologists have studied responses of both parents and siblings to the never-ending battle over toy custody, and they have discovered that when the children are left to their own devices to settle a dispute over whose toy it is, they most often settle—noisily—in favor of the toy's owner. It does help to try to get the owner to *permit* the other sib to play with it, but early on, kids know that possession is nine-tenths of the law.

TIP

315

Toddler's fracture

You'll hate this: A "toddler's fracture" is a leg fracture that occurs after a seemingly mild tumble, is characterized by a slight limp, and remains almost invisible on an X-ray initially.

Don't hyperventilate. The injury is usually a good-sized fall that requires a twisting force, such as going over a step while the body pivots over the foot. The limp is often quite pronounced, although bearing weight is possible—with pain. It doesn't take long to realize that your child has a problem, so you won't waste too much time before you're in the doctor's office or ER.

The X-ray may in fact look completely normal, but don't worry about that, either. Given the clinical picture of a toddler's fracture, most smart docs look very carefully for subtle signs of it and will usually find it. In rare instances, if the X-ray doesn't seem to show a fracture but there is real pain on walking, most doctors will assume that the toddler's fracture *is* present and treat it accordingly by placing your child in a splint and maybe on crutches and instructing you to have an orthopedist recheck the X-ray in a week, when there is a much better chance of actually seeing the fracture. A toddler's fracture heals completely in about four to six weeks.

TIP

316

Splinters

A splinter doesn't hurt until it's discovered and the child comes to the frightening realization that it needs to come out. Then it hurts, and the crying begins. In the ER, a splinter is the easiest thing in the world to handle. However, in my living room, where I frequently encounter my neighbors' children with splinters, nothing is more frustrating to manage. In the ER I have sterile equipment, local anesthetics, restraints, and people who know how to hold children. At home, conditions are less than optimal.

For this reason, except for the most superficial splinters, I don't recommend parents take out splinters at home. First, the wood softens after a few hours, and getting it out can be a painful, long procedure that involves a lot of crying, wiggling away, yelling, and tears from both ends of the needle. Second, you rarely need to remove a splinter. A thin splinter that has become embedded in the skin can be cleansed with hydrogen peroxide, kept antiseptic with an antibiotic ointment, and covered with a Band-Aid. In a few days it will migrate out along with new skin cells. If it doesn't become infected (and it shouldn't if you follow the above instructions), you have saved yourself a truly traumatic procedure.

TIP

"Use your words"

Some toddlers have learned the language of crying so well, they are reluctant to substitute words for it. Perhaps they fear that they will not be able to communicate their needs as effectively. Often these are children who are virtually silent until their second birthday, then burst forth into complex speech. If there is an older sib, a younger child's lack of speech is often attributed to his brother or sister "doing all the talking for him." (This is poppycock. Babies choose to talk or not to talk based on their own internal logic).

To enhance your toddler's desire to use his own words, the following may help:

- Listen to him with both ears.
- Ask lots of questions that require a real answer, not just yes or no: What color was the monster? Did he have lots of teeth? Or lots of noses?
- Be patient. Let him speak his piece. Nods and "uh-huhs" won't encourage him.
- If he says a word you can't understand, say it for him, or, if possible, have him point to the object and then pronounce it correctly for him.

TIP

318

Taking turns

Getting a toddler to "take turns" is a demanding way to cool crying. But in the long run, it is well worth the effort.

Rather than let a pair of eighteen-month-olds settle a dispute for themselves (despite what is said elsewhere), it is better to avoid a dispute altogether if they are not mature enough to grasp the concept of taking turns. Once they're a little more mature, try teaching them the concept in a variety of situations around the house:

- Alternate who has the first turn: "Yesterday you drank your juice first; this morning it's my turn."
- Take turns picking a toy or a book. (Make sure that when it is your turn, you pick a toy or book he likes.) He will learn the anticipation of not knowing which one you will choose and won't end up too frustrated if he doesn't get his first choice.
- Make getting dressed into a lesson: "Yesterday this shirt took a turn; today *this* shirt wants his turn."

TIP

Battleground: the stroller

One of the benefits of a lightweight, portable stroller is your ability to go from place to place relatively quickly. However, one of the last things *she* cares about is getting from place to place relatively quickly. A battle waged over getting her into the stroller may not be so much about going to the next store as it is over actually *sitting* in the stroller.

Give in on this one. Take your time. Settle for accomplishing fewer tasks on an outing, and let her push the stroller along herself if she's walking. She may not last very long at the task, particularly if it's an uphill walk or if it's a hot day. If you need to rig the game a little more in your favor, place the shopping bags you already have in the stroller and pretend that she's really pushing Baby Bop.

TIP

320

Cleaning the security blanket

No matter what security object your little girl has become attached to, she will cling to it for dear life. When she's awake. You can no more expect her to give it up to let you wash it than you can expect a chocoholic to pass up a double-fudge brownie. So don't try. But don't give up on the idea of cleaning it, either, even if she falls asleep coiled within it like a butterfly in a cocoon. Remove it gently while she's sleeping and throw it in the washer. The only thing more disgusting than a dirty security blanket is a child who carries the icky thing around with her everywhere she goes.

If you warn her in advance that you will wash it while she is asleep, she will be more tolerant when she wakes up in the morning. Then, if she gets accustomed to a blankie that smells nice, she may even ask you to wash it and may even permit washing it when she's awake.

TIP

Phone calls

If you work at home or work at maintaining an active social/volunteering/community-oriented life at home, you are probably spending a lot of time on the phone. Your toddler probably doesn't like this and may have a whole host of behaviors stored up for those moments when the phone rings and you tune him out. If you keep your priorities straight, you may be able to balance your needs and his:

- Keep a call short if it comes at a playtime.
- Give him an activity while you're on the phone. Let him know when you plan to spend a lot of time on the phone.
- Use the answering machine to screen calls, and discontinue your call waiting if you have to.
- Schedule a play date for him at a friend's house or hire a sitter if you have things you need to accomplish without interruption.

TIP

"It's time to go"

O ne of the recurring themes of this book is anticipating when crying will come and heading it off at the pass. One instance when you can anticipate a battle is when you pull a fascinated toddler away from a particularly enjoyable play date or activity.

Let him know that the good times don't go on forever. Some children just need a heads-up warning that they have to say bye-bye in five or ten minutes. Others will need a little more effort to disengage. If he is having a good time playing with another toddler or is enthralled by a particularly complicated busy-bead set, you may want to have him put the toy away before you leave. Then the transition won't seem so abrupt. Tell him that you are going to change his diaper and that the toys are going to be put away at the same time. If he's standing around bored for a minute or two, he will be happy to get into the car or stroller (where maybe he will take a nice little nap) and you can congratulate yourself on having averted a messy situation.

TIP

TV, part 1

My publisher warned me not to put this one in, but there is nothing wrong with popping a short video in or turning on a half hour of *Sesame Street* when you are absolutely exhausted and your baby has had a full day of play group, shopping, napping, splatter-the-cottage-cheese, and "let's wake up mommy." The important thing is to turn it off in half an hour, by which time you will have recharged your batteries.

Research has shown that it is not the *quality* of the TV watched that causes problems but the *quantity*. It is better, believe it or not, to watch one half hour of *Power Rangers* per day than three hours of PBS. The extra two and a half hours spent in active play far outweigh the "educational" benefit of passively watching *Arthur* or *The Magic Schoolbus* (PBS forgive me!)

TIP

324

Battleground: dressing

Before fighting this battle, understand the battle itself. Your daughter, who refuses to get dressed in the clothes you have picked out for her, or even get dressed period, is the one with the problem.

If clothes are not that important to you and she's staying home that day, pick another battle. If she has to go to her play group or to preschool, let her dress as Sleeping Beauty for the fifth day in a row. Buy her two outfits so that at least she's clean. Her teacher and other parents have seen this behavior before, and they won't think any less of you as a parent.

If she insists on wearing summer clothes in a blizzard, you can minimize the tension a bit:

- Offer her some appropriate choices. Making a choice herself will give her a victory of sorts.
- Praise the choices she does make.
- Reward speediness.
- If necessary, threaten to remove privileges.
- Hand off the chore of dressing her to dad, if he's available. Some battles are won by a changing of the guard.

TIP

"Tell me without crying"

Somehow your toddler's favorite stuffed animal ended up in her baby sister's crib, which means it ended up in her hands and mouth. Upon discovering this abomination, this miscarriage of justice, this *treachery*, your older one goes into unparalleled hysterics (and possible violence).

My wife may not have discovered the phrase "Tell me about it without crying," but she has elevated it to an art form. Hold the older child's hands, get her to look into your eyes, and then get her to take some deep breaths as she relates the ignoble deed: "Sheee… took… my… to-o-o-o-oy…"

"I still don't understand you. Tell me again. With no tears. Use all your words."

By making a project out of discussing why the baby doesn't understand ownership and by making her understand that patience is a virtue, a messy situation can be transformed into a positive, confidence-building experience.

TIP

326

Time-outs, part 1

Time-outs can be an enormously successful way to handle your toddler's tantrums, but it takes some practice to handle them correctly. First, it is a cooling-off period. Have a consistent approach as to which offenses warrant a time-out and which ones don't. When he crosses a line, inform him as to what he did wrong ("I told you not to hit your sister"), tell him he's in a time-out, and remove him to the corner or chair you have designated for the purpose. Once he's "out" (a minute per year is considered adequate), to explain again what he did wrong. Tell him that because you love him you sometimes have to use time-outs to get him to listen, and then hope that you don't have to do it all over again in five minutes.

Remember that a time-out is *his* time to compose himself. If *you* need the time-out because his normal, exuberant play is exhausting you, count to ten, and try to figure out some other activity for him that won't be so hard on you.

Most books and magazines on baby and child care give a more thorough explanation of time-outs. Donna Corwin's *The Time Out Prescription*, © 1996, is a fine book on the topic.

TIP

327

Time-outs, part 2

What if a time-out isn't working? It is usually because of one of two reasons: you or your child.

You may be the reason you aren't seeing an improvement in behavior, if you're a softie. Time-out means no fun. No talking is permitted, no TV, no kicking the wall, playing with toys, or bringing the favorite blanket (or other security object). There's also no time off for good behavior. Using a timer is often an indisputable way to make sure you both abide by the time limit.

If, on the other hand, your child is still misbehaving just as intently after a time-out or won't go into a time-out, then put him there yourself and, if necessary, enforce a "holding" time-out. My wife accomplished this by holding my son's arms stiffly at his side, refusing to let him turn around to see her, and not talking to him.

All children need to be disciplined at some point, some children more frequently than others. Often, a "holding" time-out need only be given once or twice, and your child will get the message.

TIP

328

Redirect the energy

Nothing is more frustrating than a toy that is not cooperating or a sixteen-month-old trying to play in the same room as a pair of three-year-olds. A plaintive wail fills the air as your little guy tries hard to get the blocks to stack up for the fifth time as his older brother gleefully knocks them over.

They're certainly too young to fight it out, so take one of them aside and have him help with your activity if you can. If you're in the kitchen, ask him to help you pick out the right pot to cook dinner in. If you're doing laundry, have him "sort" the shirts by colors. If you're in the garage, have him re-gap the spark plugs. You get the idea.

TIP

329

Help is coming—soon

The toddler in the midst of a tantrum, because his puzzle pieces don't fit or the tape stopped playing his favorite music, wants instant gratification, instant solutions to his problems. Understandably so—as a baby all his needs were met pretty much the moment he expressed them. Now that he can understand some words and concepts, tell him that you'll help him out *soon*. Show him the second hand on the clock, and tell him that when it's pointing straight down you'll help him.

This will refocus his attention on the clock, which he may never have thought about much before. Chances are he'll zero in so totally on the clock, that when you get there to help with the block tower, he just might brush you off.

He will only cool his heels for a little while, and you have to make sure you keep up your end of the bargain.

TIP

Make a promise you can keep

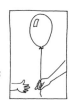

Resorting to bribery is occasionally sanctioned by the parenting-correctness police (be sure to refer to it as an "incentive" when discussing it with the other moms). After all, it is *tough* to be a one-year-old. Toys don't always cooperate, parents' moods are not always reliable, food that looks yummy turns out to be yucky. What's a toddler to do but throw a tantrum at the end of a long, hard day?

Sometimes it's perfectly okay to offer an incentive to end a tantrum. Tell him that you know he's been trying hard all day to be good, and if he can just let you finish making dinner, you'll give him his favorite dessert. Or if you're trying to finish an afternoon of shopping, offer him a special treat right off the shelf.

Why should grandparents have all the present-giving fun?

TIP

331

Anticipate an overload

Defuse a situation before it becomes a crisis. When you know what your toddler's limits for frustrations are, plan ahead and move him on to another activity before the mushroom cloud appears. If it means separating him from an older sibling or playmate, give them each a new activity. If it means turning on a TV to accomplish some goals of your own when he won't take a nap, go ahead. A half hour later he will be ready for some more active play.

If he's losing it because you've given him (or he has taken on) an activity that is beyond his developmental skills, give him something you know he can succeed at. If hunger is the issue, offer a snack so that he can go the distance.

And do a back check: Make sure that *you* are not the one heading for the overload. If you're about to fall off a cliff, give him a calmer activity so you can regroup.

TIP

332

"No" means "no"

Tough love means being tough. No one wants to see their child in the throes of a miserable tantrum, but no one wants to prolong the phase any longer than necessary. Indecisiveness or yielding to a toddler's temper is the surest way to guarantee that he will learn that if he wants something badly enough, all he has to do is scream for it. So when your son has hysterics because you have just turned off his favorite video and won't rewind it, you have to be ready to make a "No!" stick.

This is really his way of learning that there are rules to be lived by and that the sheer force of his personality is not enough to alter them. He needs to learn that if he behaves well, he gets rewarded and that bad behavior does not get rewarded. He will be much more confused about the way of the world if this basic message is not conveyed while he is young.

TIP

"I know you're angry..."

A tantrum is anger at being thwarted. And although it may not seem like it when she is yelling, crying, and kicking, there *is* a part of her brain that is receiving messages from you. It is the part that hears "Okay, you can watch TV for another hour" and tunes out "I know you are angry but I said no, already."

Take advantage of that listening capacity, and let her know that you are sorry that she is feeling this way, that you are not happy that she is so upset and angry. Negative emotions are a normal part of life; let her know that you recognize them, that will teach her to deal with bigger frustrations and disappointments that may come later on down the road.

TIP

334

Bring along the blankie

If you go away for a weekend to grandma's house or for any kind of family trip, don't forget to bring along her security blanket. You will never be able to round up another one to take its place, and she won't even think of accepting another one anyway. It will help her get to sleep while you're on the road and provide comfort in unfamiliar territory, particularly if she adapts slowly to new environments. If you plan to do some activities that are new to her, remember that the comfort of her blankie may allay her fears and help you all have more fun.

TIP

Bring the pillow, too

While you're at it, take her pillow along, too (if she uses one), since this will smooth out the rough process of adapting to a new bed. Having a familiar pillow is apt to be much more an issue for a child who has a history of being difficult with bedtime, where routine counts. To maximize your chances of your child sleeping well away from home, bring along anything that is essential to your child's bedtime routine (such as a particular book or toy).

TIP

336

Spanking

Never spank your child to discipline or punish him. This is a lousy way to teach him anything other than there are things you get spanked for and things you don't. It is not a very effective message because he will invariably misbehave when there's no one around to spank him. It also gives him a reason to dislike you or, at the very least, introduces some uncertainty into his relationship with you. He'll wonder, "Am I doing something that is going to bring out the good parent who cuddles me or the bad one who hits me?" Also, are you sure that you want to teach him that the strongest person is always the one who is right? Or that violence is *sometimes* acceptable?

TIP

337

Public tantrums

Tantrums always seem to happen during the worst possible moment for you: in a store, in the car, when you're rushing to get a meal together. Also, it is one thing to deal with them in the privacy of your own family room, but quite another to face public scrutiny.

You probably have the expectation that when in public, you need to (1) be a sensible, giving parent, but still (2) keep the noise down. But there are times when you'll need to play the heavy. When he is screaming in the supermarket for the candy bar that dad always buys him, if you have already said "no," you mean NO. Don't back down, even if he is screaming like a banshee and you find yourself surrounded by concerned (or irritated) faces. Finish checking out, get in the car, and get him home. The next time you go into the store, don't be surprised if people congratulate you on your firmness and even say wistfully, "I wish I could be that consistent with my kids!"

And don't be surprised if checking out is much, much quieter next time.

TIP

"Act like a big boy (or girl)"

A one-year-old is still a baby. If he is crying because he's hurt, frustrated, or doesn't want to see you go out for the evening, don't tell him to "act like a big boy." Chances are, he has seen lots of bigger boys crying over similar things, so your admonition just won't make any sense to him. Also, he does not have the rational capacity to think of himself as a big boy any more than he can reflect on how he used to act as a four-month-old.

Kiss the boo-boo, hug him through the tantrum, wave bye-bye as you and daddy go out on a much-needed date, and promise him lots of hugs and kisses when you get back.

"That's silly!"

Just as it is not fair to your son to expect him to act like a grown-up when he is crying over a minor boo-boo, it's not fair to tell him that he's being silly if he's crying over a seemingly insignificant problem. The process of gaining independence is a long, hard climb with lots of scrapes along the way and lots of time needed for a breather. So when, at the end of a long day, he has a meltdown because the french fries are the wrong shape, let him have his little cry, and remind him that they will taste just the same. Pop one in your mouth, make an excited or animal noise, and turn eating into a game instead.

TIP

340

Force-feeding

Never force your child to clean a plate (or highchair top) or punish him for not eating. You may need to coax and cajole him just to sit calmly for a meal, only to see him lose interest after one or two reluctant bites of his favorite food. Since it is important to him to see that everybody eats as a family (if, in fact, your family has the luxury of sitting together to eat), it is better to have him sit and watch you eat when he's not hungry. Don't push more food into him than he can tolerate. This leads to obesity in the long run, as it is possible to overcome the sense of fullness that limits appetite and helps him regulate calorie intake. Fat babies are fine, but fat toddlers may be headed for trouble.

TIP

341

Dinnertime tantrums

Does the sight of meatloaf on her plate send her into a frenzy? Does tuna casserole on the table make her pull her hair? This goes beyond just not eating. We're talking about a bout of hysterics because the mere *presence* of certain foods offends her sense of propriety. Do you:

(a) Feed her something else (although there is no guarantee she'll eat it).
(b) Continue to offer the same food you're all eating.
(c) Let her leave the table.
(d) Try all of the above.

The answer is (d). If she's had a bad day, it may be appropriate to her mood and the circumstances to allow her a little leeway (a). Go ahead and offer her something she'll like. If she refuses a favorite food, on the other hand, then go to plan (b). She's trying to establish the right to change her mind, but you don't have to give in. Then opt for choice (c). Remember, she'll eat when she's hungry.

Don't you just hate pop quizzes?

TIP

Don't overbook his day

I t's one thing if *your* daily schedule is overbooked. Don't overload your child's day with so many events that she's fried by noon. If she's crying because she has to leave a play date (where she's having fun) just to go to another friend's house, consider it a warning sign.

Some children get irritable with other children when they're tired or overstimulated. If she's the kind of girl who can have fun with just one playmate per morning, don't overextend her patience. If *you* are the one who wants or needs to catch up with your friends, do it one at a time. An unhappy, tired, or frustrated toddler is going to take most of the fun out of the visit anyway.

TIP

343

TV, part 2

At some point along the way, I am contractually obligated to make a plug for Adams Media's companion publication, *365 TV-Free Activities You Can Do With Your Child*. Don't calm your crying kid by turning the TV on. There are at least 365 other things you can do instead.

TIP

344

Tantrums and allergies

Is an allergy contributing to your toddler's terrible behavior? While the typical allergic symptoms of wheezing, stomach upset, and eye/nasal congestion are well known, it is possible that central nervous system responses to allergens include irritability, even without any of these other symptoms.

If your toddler has suddenly revved up the flinging, hitting, and screaming, consider possible environmental influences: a new pet in the house, a new food group (nuts, dairy, shellfish), or even the season. It can take time to isolate the cause, but if there *is* a family history of allergy or your baby has had wheezing, eczema, or other allergy symptoms in the past, the time is well spent. As with other allergies, the primary treatment is removing the offending agent.

TIP

345

Control their environment

"I'll put myself in time-out, thank you very much!"

Sometimes it may seem as if your child deliberately misbehaves. Could he be possessed by a demon? You may think that I'm talking about his exhibiting a nasty, forbidden behavior (pushing the baby over, throwing the bowl of soup on the floor, magic marker on the walls) followed by cries of "Time out! Time out!" and then a dash to the time-out corner. (It may truly be demonic possession, don't get me wrong.)

But it may also be a technique of exerting control over his environment. He is showing you multiple things: that he understands what bad behavior is and that he is aware of the consequences of bad behavior.

You may never get so far ahead of the game that you can always control his impulses toward misbehavior, but you should still stick to your principles. Give him the time-out he demands, extend the period if necessary, and take away a privilege if he continues to misbehave. And recognize the silver lining for what it is: a sign that your efforts at discipline are really paying off.

TIP

346

Preparing an older sib for the new baby

If you plan to put your older child in daycare or preschool when your new baby is born, start him there before the new baby is born. This way he will have a routine activity to help him occupy his time without mommy, and he will get used to having less mommy time. He also won't spend all his time crying for attention—just like the newborn does. If he needs to give up a pacifier or finish potty training, it will be easier without sibling rivalry to distract him.

Be aware, though, that once the big day of the new baby's homecoming arrives, he may try to get your attention by acting just like baby, by soiling his pants or returning to his pacifier.

One thing that might help his adjustment is giving him a toy baby that can be his to take care of before the big day arrives. This way, when you come home, you can *both* change your babies' diapers or give them a feeding. Some of the natural frustration he will feel can be deflected by having him do some activities that parallel your own.

TIP

347

Making medicine yummy

An inescapable side effect of most medicines is their nasty taste. This is why parents need to be creative to get it down and partly why drug companies go to great lengths to reduce the number of times per day that they need to be taken. Some pharmacies (usually independent ones) will do you the favor of adding flavor to some of their vilest concoctions. A pharmacist in Washington, D.C., has devised a recipe book that allows forty-two different flavors to be mixed into most children's medicines (Sorry, I checked—there's no Rocky Road). It's called FLAVORx and may add $1–$5 to the cost of your medicine (a small price to pay if your child likes the taste better).

Your pharmacy or doctor can call 1-800-884-5771 if they are not familiar with FLAVORx or cannot come up with an equally tempting concoction.

Another tip for giving medicine

Your toddler need never cry over taking medicine—if he never even knows he's taking it.

One favorite doctor's tip for getting kids to take medicine is to mix it into applesauce or juice. But chances are your child will recognize the taste anyway and will refuse it.

Try giving your child something salty, such as potato chips, to eat first. He will, without a doubt, welcome the opportunity for some junk food. But it will get him thirsty enough so that you can now get the medicine in. Either give it to him straight or mix it with a little juice (not a lot, so that you don't have to force him to drink the whole thing).

I credit my wife with discovering this trick, which has been phenomenally successful in our household.

TIP

349

Febrile seizures

Once again, I'm stepping into an area that doesn't immediately involve crying, but this is important: From fifteen months to five years, a sudden fever can cause seizures. This occurs in about 1 percent of all children. The most common type of febrile seizure is a "simple" one: an episode of generalized rhythmic contractions lasting three to five minutes, followed by a period of unconsciousness of no more than five to ten minutes. The temperature, when taken, is often 104°F or more. A doctor will generally only diagnose a febrile seizure if he has ruled out the following neurological conditions: epilepsy (check your family history), developmental delays, or earlier seizures.

Simple febrile seizures represent the body's response to a rapid rise in temperature. They do *not* indicate meningitis, and they do *not* cause brain damage. Period.

The doctor should look for the cause of the infection. If it is a virus (certain ones such as the virus that causes roseola are common culprits), no antibiotics are needed. For the next two or three days, all you should do is keep your child's temperature down with the recommended doses of Tylenol or ibuprofen. Aspirin is not used for fever in children anymore.

TIP

350

Mouth injuries

Until someone invents an antigravity device made specifically for toddlers, what goes up will come down. When putting an arm out doesn't serve to break a fall, a top-heavy twelve- to eighteen-month-old will almost always fall forward onto their face. The mouth is particularly prone to injuries, most of which are, fortunately, benign despite what they look like at first.

A cut inside the mouth or a knocked-out tooth is messy, bloody, painful, and frightening for all concerned. An intact primary (baby) tooth that gets knocked out may be placed back in the mouth if it is out for less than thirty minutes. The permanent (adult) tooth is in the socket and will preserve the tooth space. A broken tooth requires the attention of a dentist. A cut inside the mouth will heal but may require a soft diet for a few days (no pizza or other food that requires the use of the lips to hold on while the teeth tear into it). Give lots of fluids through a straw and mushy foods like Jell-O, pudding, applesauce, etc.

A cut on the outer lip that needs stitches will have the longest consequences because it leaves a visible scar. A plastic surgeon is generally needed if it crosses the "vermilion border," the border between the lip margin and the skin.

TIP

Nursemaid elbow

The forearm has two bones, the radius and ulna. The radius is the one that goes along the thumb side of the arm and is the shorter of the two. The head of the radius fits into a notch in the ulna just below the elbow and may become subluxed, or slightly dislocated, with forceful twisting. The event itself is frequently not seen or recognized: The child may be pulled by the arm, or it may get caught in the couch or between slats in the crib. After the injury, a child typically holds her arm slightly flexed at the elbow and with her hand slightly curled resting near her hip. She will not raise it up from there for anything: her blankie, her mommy, nothing.

Curiously, if you ask her where it hurts, she will point to her wrist or shoulder but rarely to the elbow itself. Another important feature is a complete lack of bruising or swelling in the affected area.

This is *very* easily treated in the ER or by your doctor, and I will not divulge the secret in print for one simple reason: *Just in case* it's a broken bone, I don't want you to play around with it any more than you need to. (Also, parents always look on their doctor like a hero when it's fixed, and I hate to deprive my fellow pediatricians and family docs of that kind of adulation.)

TIP

352

External ear infections

O*titis externa* is an infection of the outer ear. This ear infection usually spares the middle ear and is characterized by reddening of the ear itself. Sometimes the ear itself bulges outward, and there is often a thick mucusy-cheesy discharge. Looking into the ear will often be a painful experience.

It arises from submerging the ears under water and allowing the ever-present germs to grow in the soupy mixture of water, wax, and shed skin cells. It takes about a day to develop, and kids absolutely howl with this. Forget childbirth; ear infections *hurt*!

The treatment is with antibiotics, steroids, and analgesic ear drops (such as Auralgan or Cortisporin), which your doctor can prescribe for you. As always, give Tylenol or ibuprofen for anything acutely painful.

TIP

353

Sinusitis

Sinusitis is a bacterial infection of the paranasal sinuses (located near the cheeks and mid-lower forehead). It is further defined as symptoms of a cold, such as nasal discharge, cough, fever, and midfacial pain, that persist for more than nine days. Symptoms of lesser duration do *not* indicate sinusitis, but this is a controversial area. Predisposing factors of sinusitis include:

- A past or present nasal obstruction, such as a foreign body, or enlarged adenoids
- Increased mucus: A cold, upper respiratory infection, allergy, exposure to pet dander, or secondhand cigarette smoke.

Many parents are under the impression that a runny nose with green discharge is sinusitis, but this is a myth. Most colds produce a clear, runny nose for two or three days. Then, as the body works to rid the virus, it produces immune cells which can turn the mucus green. This phase lasts for a day or two, and then the cold is over. Just as Mother Nature intended: without antibiotics.

TIP

354

Urinary tract infection (UTI)

This one is for girls only. A urinary tract infection is a minor but painful illness. Girls have a shorter urethra than boys—the tube that goes from the bladder to the outside—just short enough to permit bacteria to travel upstream into the bladder. The urine in the bladder is a good growth medium for bacteria, and the result is a urine infection.

Where do the bacteria come from? Dirty diapers. The bacteria that are normally present in stool are responsible for 90 percent of bladder infections. This means that an episode of diarrhea might predispose her to a urinary infection. (So does wiping her from back to front—*always* wipe a girl from front to back).

The symptoms of a UTI are not very specific: tummy ache, crying, and often fever. If you are astute enough or your girl is verbal enough, you might be able to pick up on worse pain with urination or occasionally a foul smell to the urine.

The treatment is generally a short course of antibiotics, after which your doctor may want to schedule some tests to make sure there are no anatomic factors predisposing her to a repeat infection.

TIP

355

Vaginitis

Vaginitis, another condition that affects girls exclusively, causes a painful, itchy rash and discharge. Although the finding of any kind of rash in a young girl's diaper area is a cause for concern, the reason is usually quite innocuous. Girls rub themselves and sometimes develop a break in the skin that allows infection. If she was rubbing her runny nose and then touches her labia, she can transmit some common cold germs to an area that is susceptible to those bacteria. Or, if she is trying to toilet-train herself, she may have left a small piece of tissue paper behind, which can lead to infection. Finally, girls are just as curious as boys about their own bodies. Just as some girls place beads in their nose, this too is a cavity that invites experimentation.

Vaginitis is treated with a topical antibiotic cream or ointment and removal of the offending foreign body if one is present. This is a condition that should be evaluated by your doctor.

If there is even a remote concern that this condition is a result of a molestation, your doctor is the one to begin to help you evaluate that possibility. For the moment, however, be reassured that the signs of child sexual assault are *behavioral* far more often than physical, and that a vaginitis is a common, benign problem.

TIP

Balanitis and paraphimosis

Okay, boys, now it's your turn. There are a couple of painful problems that can affect male toddlers. Balanitis is an inflammation of the foreskin that may extend to involve the head (glans) of the penis. It is most commonly caused by bacteria or yeast and looks diffusely red and swollen. Paraphimosis is an obstruction of blood flow from a constricted ring of retracted foreskin. This in turn leads to swelling of the foreskin and underlying glans. It is sometimes caused by balanitis or by phimosis, the inability of the distal foreskin to be retracted over the glans. By itself, phimosis is not painful and results from failure to pull the foreskin back over the glans after manually retracting it for penile cleaning. (It can also be caused by boys who experiment with their parts.)

Either condition should be examined by a physician. If the tip of the penis is exposed by a foreskin that does not retract by itself *but is not painful or swollen*, you can fix it at home this way: Put your thumb over the tip of the penis, and pull the foreskin forward until it returns to its normal position. Your son may protest, but it should help him. If not, or if adjusting the foreskin seems too painful for him, call your doctor.

TIP

Chicken pox

Chicken pox ought to be a disappearing disease. It's not. The disease pattern is classic, and the rash is absolutely distinctive: small red dots that grow, blister, and scab over. There are frequently two or three "crops" of lesions, and they are *itchy*, seemingly more so when they scab over. Itchy almost always leads to crying.

Since chicken pox is transmitted exclusively from person to person, it is an ideal candidate to vaccinate out of existence. A vaccine was finally licensed by the FDA in 1996 after years of research. It has not caught on as well as many pediatricians thought it would, but general acceptance of it is growing.

If your child is age one to thirteen years old and has not had a varicella vaccine, he/she should receive it. If your child is older than thirteen and has never had chicken pox, two doses are needed. Chicken pox is a much more severe illness in adolescence or adulthood and has a higher rate of complications. If *you* have never had chicken pox yourself, consider being vaccinated as well.

TIP

If your child comes in contact with anyone who has an immune deficiency (AIDS, cancer requiring chemotherapy), it will protect that person as well, since chicken pox can be fatal if the immune system is functioning poorly.

358

12–24 MONTHS: TODDLERHOOD

Go online

No matter when you need help, the Internet is always there. Whether you sign on to one of the many parental advice or support groups to get more ideas on how to manage your baby, send E-mail to a friend or relative, or leave all the cares of parenthood behind and assume the persona of an eighty-seven-year-old federal penitentiary inmate discussing the pros and cons of eighteenth-century animists, you can find your niche and recharge your batteries in time for the next auditory assault. Some helpful sites are:

- **www.aap.org** The American Academy of Pediatrics.
- **www.parenthoodweb.com** Pediatricians and psychiatrists help answer your questions.
- **www.parenting-qa.com** Offers even more broad-based Q&A help than the previous site.
- **www.parentsplace.com** A popular site with lots of links.
- **www.zerotothree.org** An advocacy group that focuses on development and social issues.

TIP

359

Hotlines

For the fourteen families out there who still are not online, you can still pick up the phone and communicate with real people, too. If your question is not an immediate health question (for which your doctor is still the first one to turn to), there are places where you can find information, support and advocacy groups:

- 1-800-4-A-CHILD (422-4453). Twenty-four-hour advice from a national ChildHelp crises hotline staffed by people with graduate degrees in counseling. They can answer questions from preventing child abuse to social concerns.
- 1-800-583-4135. The National Parent Information Network (M–F, 8 A.M.–5 P.M., PST). As the name says, this network will track down *any* information a parent needs free of charge.
- 1-800-704-2102. The Single Parents Association (M–F, 8 A.M.–5 P.M., PST). For the parent going at it alone, this is the place to turn for local resources, support groups, and answers when no one else is immediately at hand.

TIP

360

Magazines

Perhaps because I'm a pediatrician, I receive tons of parent/baby-oriented magazines each month. They sit in a large stack next to my medical journals (which also accumulate at an equally daunting rate). These are wonderful resources for parenting advice. If none of my recommendations for calming your baby work, try these:

- *Parents*
- *Working Mother*
- *Sesame Street Parents*
- *American Baby*
- *Parenting*
- *Child*

They all generally follow a similar format: letters directed toward solving a particular issue; warm, instructive anecdotal experiences; professional advice on developmental, medical, or behavioral issues, often with details by age group; and consumer advice on everything from household baby products to toys to books and games. While you may not need to hang onto every article in every magazine, a quick, five-minute perusal of any current issue ought to provide you with some new ideas for calming a crier.

TIP

361

Juicy poops

Diaper rashes are a painful, unwelcome ailment in toddlers who have frequent, wet stools, also known as the "juicy poops." Not only the rash, but the accompanying intestinal discomfort contribute to tears. The cause is often an easily remediable dietary problem.

Toddlers who decide for themselves what to eat or drink often go for the juice—with full parental consent. Juice, although nutritious, is full of sugar. "Toddler trots" can result from a huge load of sugar that goes straight through baby's intestinal system without being absorbed. All this sugar pulls water into the intestine along with it and results in sloppy, slimy stools and rashes and doesn't really nourish him. His tummy gets filled up, but the calories are lacking.

Try a dilute sport drink (Gatorade) instead. These provide less sugar and are more readily absorbed, causing less overall hunger (or thirst).

Limit the amount of juice he drinks. If he sees that his rash fades away, he may even internalize the message and stop asking for so much juice.

TIP

Hair pulling

Hair pulling is a somewhat common behavior in older infants and toddlers. *You* know the feeling of wanting to pull your hair out; so does your baby; the only difference is that she *does* it. As you might imagine, it is a sign of frustration or anger. It appears at the end of the day when everything is going wrong and is accompanied by throwing toys, food (if the mood happens to catch her in the highchair), or pulling at clothes.

She may have started this out as a self-stimulating activity, like rocking or head banging. And, like these, she can go too far and actually hurt herself in the process.

The answer is no more (or less) complicated than removing her from whatever is frustrating her, calming her down, and letting the storm pass. When she's a little older, you should be able to give her some other way to cope with frustration, such as punching a pillow or tearing on an old towel.

TIP

How to use a crying baby

Nobody wants to be on line at the supermarket. If you only have four or five items and the line for the express checkout is a mile long, the people on line will often let you and your hyper-decibel wailer sail right to the front of the line. It is probably unwise to point this out to them, but a few minutes at the back of the line should be all it takes. (You may have to make some ineffectual gestures toward calming the crying, so be sure to make it clear that you don't have a *clue* in the world how to quiet your baby.)

TIP
364

The final word

The final word can only be this: In time, your baby *will* stop crying so much. While this achievement may seem incredibly far off—a gleaming light at the end of a long, dark tunnel—take a moment to look at it from the perspective of that distant day. It will seem almost unbelievable to you that your baby was so small—so fat, pink, and full of wonder at the world. You'll remember a time before she could speak, before she could walk or even crawl, before she could grab a rattle, shake it, and squeal with delight, before she could even prop her head up on her little chubby arms, when she managed to sprinkle in between those cries, which were never really so troublesome after all, the most precious jewel of her untroubled, unexpected beautiful smile.

TIP

365

ALSO AVAILABLE FROM
ADAMS MEDIA CORPORATION

365 Outdoor Activities You Can Do With Your Child
1-55850-260-2, $6.95

365 TV-Free Activities You Can Do With Your Child
1-55850-585-7, $7.95

Available wherever books are sold.

HOW TO ORDER: If you cannot find these titles at your favorite retail outlet, you may order them directly from the publisher. BY PHONE: Call 1-800-872-5627. We accept Visa, Mastercard, and American Express. $4.95 will be added to your total order for shipping and handling. BY MAIL: Write out the full titles of the books you'd like to order and send payment, including $4.95 for shipping and handling, to: Adams Media Corporation, 260 Center Street, Holbrook, MA 02343. 30-day money-back guarantee.

ALSO AVAILABLE FROM
ADAMS MEDIA CORPORATION

Ain't Misbehavin'
The 10 Discipline Issues Every Parent Faces and How to Resolve Them
Dr. William P. Garvey
1-55850-805-8, $9.95

No more whining! No more arguments! No more tantrums! *Ain't Misbehavin'* gives parents invaluable advice for dealing with the ten most common behavior problems—from bedtime arguments to temper tantrums. *Ain't Misbehavin'* gives you the help you need to feel more confident and capable of disciplining your child and shows you how you can develop a less combative, more harmonious parent-child relationship.

Available wherever books are sold.

HOW TO ORDER: If you cannot find these titles at your favorite retail outlet, you may order them directly from the publisher. BY PHONE: Call 1-800-872-5627. We accept Visa, Mastercard, and American Express. $4.95 will be added to your total order for shipping and handling. BY MAIL: Write out the full titles of the books you'd like to order and send payment, including $4.95 for shipping and handling, to: Adams Media Corporation, 260 Center Street, Holbrook, MA 02343. 30-day money-back guarantee.

Acknowledgments

I am grateful for the assistance of a number of people who have shaped this book. First of course, is my wife Hindy, the inspiration and teacher of our entire family. Lord knows, she has thrown herself into the line of fire far more times than can ever be counted, often so that I could put to print yet another crying tip. This is a conflict of interest that will keep the ethicists going for years.

I would also like to acknowledge the efforts of my agent, Jeanne Hanson, and editor Pam Liflander of Adams Media who together managed to keep this project on track and jump started it when it seemed to be irrevocably stalled.

Finally, thanks go to the moms of Potomac, Maryland whose advice and comments I mined religiously for the interesting and unusual pet methods that appear herein. I had a list of all your names but my computer crashed, taking all of them down with it . . .